Unknown Justice

by

Kelly Fox

DORRANCE PUBLISHING CO., INC.
PITTSBURGH, PENNSYLVANIA 15222

The contents of this work including, but not limited to, the accuracy of events, people, and places depicted; opinions expressed; permission to use previously published materials included; and any advice given or actions advocated are solely the responsibility of the author, who assumes all liability for said work and indemnifies the publisher against any claims stemming from publication of the work.

Dorrance Publishing Co., Inc.
701 Smithfield Street
Pittsburgh, PA 15222
Visit our website at *www.dorrancebookstore.com*

ISBN: 978-1-4349-0706-6
eISBN: 978-1-4349-2358-5

This book is dedicated to my son and daughter, Mark and Katie, as named in the book. I love and respect these two children for the strength and endurance they have passed on to me through our lives of turmoil and heartache. I am a teacher, but my greatest lessons have come from my own two children. The shame, humiliation, and wrongdoing thrust upon them during their young lives was inexcusable and inhumane. I am proud of my grown up children, for their lives, and the kindness and compassion they show towards others even when they did not always receive this in their younger days. I love you guys!

In the Beginning

Chapter One

On July 13, 1980, my lifetime boyfriend since the third grade and I were married in the small country church wherein we were both raised—Adams Grove Baptist Church. We had both gone to school together since elementary and graduated from the same college, and then we were married.

Dallas Lowell Phillips was one of four children. He was next to the oldest child. His oldest brother, Ernie Dalton Phillips, was killed in an automobile accident when he was only eighteen years old. D.L., as his closest friends and family called him, was only sixteen at the time. D.L had two younger sisters, Carolyn and Vivian, the latter better known as "Bee Bee."

We spent our honeymoon in a neighboring hotel on the Atlantic Ocean in Virginia Beach. The Thunderbird Hotel was located right on the beach. Our honeymoon began with a tragedy when my new husband began laughing at me upon my entrance into the bedroom. I was wearing a black lace negligee that had been a gift from a close friend at my premarital lingerie party. I spent most of our wedding night crying because of his unforgiving laughter. The honeymoon was mostly ritual rather than spontaneous and passionate lovemaking.

The first two or three years of our marriage were like a bad dream, as well as a new experience for me. I had gone from a secure, warm, loving home to a cold, rude awakening of uncertainty and heartache. D.L. had no sense of feeling or compassion.

Our marriage was one of no intimacy, basically just routine. We arose each morning, went to work, returned home, ate dinner, retired to our bed, and usually lay awake until we both fell asleep. That's it in a nutshell.

I finally convinced D.L. that we were both not getting any younger and I wanted to have children. After a few months of debating, he agreed to try. The sex was strictly business with no extras.

The baby was due on December 10, 1985. By December 20, there was no baby. Dr. Sam Grizzard Jr. told me I would be admitted in the hospital on the morning after Christmas Day. D.L. and I got up at about 5:30 AM. I was admitted at about 7:00 AM. For three days, the doctors tried to induce labor. Nothing happened. Finally, at about 5:00 PM. on December 28, the doctor came and told me we could still continue the attempt to induce, or I could choose the option of cesarean. I chose the latter because I was worn out and wanted a baby to hold. I was taken into surgery at about 6:35 that evening, and, shortly after, a 9 ½ pounds bouncing baby boy was born. The baby was fine. Everyone thought Mom was doing well, but I felt miserable. The rest of that night was vague due to sedation. When it was time for the baby to be fed, I tried to breastfeed him. However, it was not very successful. In a couple of days, Mark Dalton Phillips and I were released from the hospital. I felt very weak and had a low-grade fever. I was extremely uncomfortable, and I could not understand why they were sending me home.

The next month was a slow one. I could not nurse the baby. I had to resort to bottle-feeding. My days were very long and weary, and there was a pain in my side. It would not stop, but my husband was not concerned. He did assist with changing the baby's diaper once in a while, and late night feedings. D.L. seemed to be proud of his new son; however, this did not improve our relations to any great extent. The days and nights would come and go. Most of my nights were spent with me waking up in cold sweats. My gown and the bed would be soaked and wet, and I would have to get up and change gowns. Again, D.L. was not concerned, and so, I avoided trying to draw attention to the matter.

Finally, my mother was visiting one day, and I told her about how horrible I felt. She immediately responded by saying, "Sharon, you need to go back to your doctor. Don't wait around. Something's wrong!"

A call was made, and the appointment was scheduled for the following week. My Aunt Virginia (my mother's sister) drove me to Petersburg, Virginia where the Gyn building was located. After getting settled in the waiting room, it was only a few minutes before I was called back to the patient room. Dr. Grizzard Jr. told me to lie still for a minute, that he wanted his father to look at it. When he pushed on one spot under my right breast, it nearly sent me through the floor; the pain was excruciating.

Dr. Grizzard Sr. was my mother's doctor when I was born. He worked in the same office as his son but no longer saw as many patients. They both returned. Dr. Grizzard Sr. sort of poked me in the initial spot. Again, I nearly went through the table because of the unbearable pain. I was then told I would have to go to the neighboring hospital—Southside Regional Medical Center—for a sonogram. Aunt Gin, as I called her, carried me over to the hospital. She was a nervous wreck. On top of this, we had to wait for what seemed to be an eternity. It was getting later in the afternoon, and I was getting tired and worried. My Aunt Gin was almost in tears. The sonogram was taken. About twenty minutes later, Dr. Gizzard came up to Aunt Gin and I in the waiting area. He looked at me and said, "We are going to have to admit that you have a large 'mass' of something, and we are not sure what it is." I knew I could not show my fear because Aunt Gin would become hysterical. All I could do was keep my composure. After all, I had a one-month-old baby at home. Who would take care of him? Suppose I never get to see him again? This and many more questions were making my head swirl. I remarked that I had no clothes with me and mentioned going home to get them. Dr. Grizzard frowned and remarked, "I really do not think that is a good idea. The bumpy streets and secondary roads may cause the 'mass' to burst, and this could be very dangerous." Aunt Gin agreed to go home, call my mother, and have her bring me back some clothes. So it was. My mother was exasperated. Upon her arrival, she smiled and tried to appear calm, but the agitation was quite obvious between the smiles and nods of her head. Eventually, she adjusted to the horror as best she could and resorted to leave and go back home for the night.

The early evening was spent with fairly nice, warm treatment by the nurses. Dr. Grizzard dropped by and told me a surgeon, Dr. Smith, would be dropping by either later that evening or the next morning. Sure enough, sometime between 9:00 and 10:00 P.M. that evening, Dr. Smith arrived. He came over to my bed and began pushing around on my abdomen. All of a sudden, he made a fist and placed it in a spot on my upper abdomen. Then he took his other hand, made another fist, and hit the fist that was already in place on my rib cage. I could not believe he had done that. It did not hurt as much as it stunned and shocked me. Then he broke the news: I would have to have surgery the next morning, around 7:00 A.M. I notified my mother by phone. The next morning was a continuous nightmare. I had to be given a couple of pints of blood because my blood count was not acceptable for surgery. Upon receiving the blood, I was rushed to the emergency room for surgery. By the time they had given me the blood, my mother, father, D.L., and two close friends I had grown up with, Linda and Bootsie, were all present. I had no siblings, and Linda and Bootsie usually stayed at my house, or I spent weekends at their house when we were growing up. I was really scared. The terrifying reality of possibly not making it through the operation was a constant threat to me. Then the anesthesia came. I was going, going gone.

I was not feeling well when I finally came to consciousness sometime later that night; I was drifting in and out of sleep. The next day, they began noticing that my stomach was swelling. They also informed me that a tube would have to be inserted through my nose, down to my stomach. I said confidently, "Well, at least I will be put to sleep."

The nurse reluctantly replied, "No, you have to be awake because we will insert the tube through your nose, and you will have to take slow swallows until it reaches your stomach."

No! This can't be happening right now, I thought." The pain and discomfort as the tube was being inserted through my nose and throat was humiliating and overwhelming to say the least. I asked to have no visitors for the next day or two because of the way I felt and looked. After a long fourteen days, I returned home to continue my motherhood with a brand new baby that I hardly recognized. Mark had grown so much that it was like starting all over again. My body was okay but, surgically, lacking a gallbladder.

Reality Sets In

Chapter Two

At three years of age, Mark had grown into an adorable, precious human being. It was time for nursery school, which was none other than Miss Paula's Playhouse. My friends had enrolled their children in Miss Paula's, and it was considered to be the cream of the crop of all nursery schools in our local hometown of Emporia, Virginia.

After about a year in nursery school, Miss Paula sent me a note requesting a conference. I met with her one morning before I went to work. Her concerns were resolved around her observations of Mark. He was a loner; he did not mingle easily and willingly with other children. The coloring, cutting, and simple preschool exercises, Mark was unable to do. She recommended that he be tested to find out why he was behind others his age. Because of the fact that I was already a certified special education teacher in the Greensville County Public School system, the testing process went rather smoothly. It was also completed in a timely fashion. Deborah Rullman, a friend and local school psychologist, called me in for a meeting following the testing. She explained in detail Mark's intellectual function. First of all, he had a full scale IQ (intelligence quotient) below seventy. Second, she admitted that Mark was extremely nervous during testing. She suggested he had learning problems but was uncertain what percentage consisted of lack of aptitude. She suggested we keep monitoring his performance and perhaps enroll Mark in an early childhood special education program offered in public schools.

Upon Mark's graduation from nursery school, we followed the suggested procedure and enrolled him in an early childhood education program. Mark spent part of the day in the early childhood program and a portion of the day in a regular kindergarten class. The kindergarten teacher described Mark as being very much on guard constantly and still behind in academic skills. He was very reluctant to play and socialize with other children.

In the meantime, we decided that Mark should get involved in extracurricular activities to provide him with further opportunities to be around other children. His father had been a baseball player in high school and had every dream of his son following his footsteps. The first time D.L. practiced tee-ball with Mark was a disaster. When his father threw the ball and Mark could not catch it, D.L. went into a rage. It was as though he expected this little five-year-old boy to automatically be a champion baseball player. He projected both shame and anger to Mark. Unfortunately, similar acts occurred when Mark's father tried to teach him how to hit the ball with the bat. If Mark missed twice in a row, his father would throw the ball and glove down and leave Mark and me standing in the yard. He acted like a spoiled brat although he was the adult and Mark was the child. Mark could have been a good ball player if his father had given him a chance. We attended tee-ball games, and Mark could actually hit the ball harder than any other child on his team (when he hit it). With a little patience and time, he could have possibly excelled in this area. After one year of tee-ball, it ended up being the only extracurricular activity Mark ever participated in until later in high school.

From then on, D.L. was always ashamed of his son. Mark had been identified as a child with learning problems, and his father hated it. He never accepted or dealt with the diagnosis, even though D.L. himself had learning problems, as a young boy. Easy is the best way of life. However, the situation went from bad to worse.

On May 20, 1989, Mark became the brother to a beautiful eight pounds and thirteen ounces sister. Katherine Fox Phillips was born vaginally; no surgery had to be performed. The first six months following Katie's birth, D.L.'s attitude seemed to somewhat change. He was even a little more attentive to me for a while. Katie was a precious, blond, curly-haired daughter, and her father adored her. Then the bombshell was dropped. Katie went to Miss Paula's Playhouse, and once again, the inevitable happened. Similar delayed behaviors as with Mark were observed in Katie. Not only did D.L. have one child with handicapping conditions but two. He was totally devastated. By this point, our marriage was barely hanging by a thread. First, there was Mark, and then, Katie's diagnosis of developmental impairment had shattered any hopes and dreams parents could have for their children and themselves. D.L.'s daily routine began with one of later and later getting home from work. Then he would go into an outrage if I asked why he was late. I quickly learned not to question him and blindly assumed he was being honest when he told me he had paperwork and problems that came up after his 8:00 A.M. to 4:00 P.M. workday, preventing him from getting home until 6:00 or 6:30 P.M.

D.L. had been promoted from a supervisor over inmates at a local prison sewage treatment plant to a supervisor over several sewage treatment plants in the eastern region of our Virginia Department of Corrections. He also informed me that he was moving his office from Southampton Correctional

Center, which was only five or six miles from our home, to Suffolk, which was almost forty-five to fifty miles from our home. I questioned why he preferred to drive further from home to work each day, and he responded that he would have a much nicer and bigger office in Suffolk. They were also providing him with a state vehicle he could drive back and forth to work each day. Once again, this loving, devoted, Christian wife and mother believed another one of her husband's cock and bull stories.

Transition

Chapter Three

The next few years, 1980 to 1993, I became extremely involved and dedicated to the Emporia Junior Woman's Club.

I was also considering working on a master's degree in special education at a neighboring university. D.L. agreed to babysit one night a week for approximately two years while I worked on my master's degree. I had worked my way up first to vice president in the Emporia Junior Woman's Club. The next year, I would officially be installed as president. However, I chose to give up the presidency of the club that forthcoming year to work on completing my thesis for a master's degree at Virginia State University in Colonial Heights, Virginia. After a couple of years in the master's program, I received my master's degree in special education, July 1996.

I was extremely proud of my master's degree and so was my father. He was the one who always encouraged and praised me when I met goals or accomplishments in life. For the most part, Daddy supported me in whatever I sought out to do in my life as long as it was prosperous and something I chose to do. My father was always the backbone of my professional and social careers. He loved me, protected my interests, and endeavored only to increase and heighten my confidence from the time I was born until the day he died. Daddy would always say, "I'm so proud of you, sweetie. I don't know what to do!" Sometimes, he would call me "Daught," nickname for "my daughter."

Shortly after receiving my master's degree, D.L. went on his annual Memorial Day fishing trip to Suffolk, Virginia, with close fishing and hunting buddies. It was a men's trip, but he never wanted Mark to go with him on these fishing trips. I never could understand why until Memorial Day weekend, 1996. D.L. returned from his fishing trip and threw his dirty pants on the bed. I began to gather his dirty clothes from the fishing trip, emptying out pockets in his shirts and pants. D.L. conveniently wandered outside while I gathered his dirty clothes for washing. I found a note in one pocket of his pants. The note read: "Oh, Darling, I have missed you so much. I love you more than anything else in the world. I will see you at 3:45 this afternoon. I look forward to seeing you."

I went to the backdoor and called D.L. He came in, and I coldly approached him about what I had found in his pocket. Apparently, D.L. had wanted me to find the note. However, he feebly began to explain that the note was one from an affair with a woman he had met at the Suffolk office a year ago. To make a long story short, I kicked his "royal behind" out. I told him that I thought he and I needed time to think about our actions and what we really wanted. He admitted having an affair, packed up, and left to go to his mother's house. Before leaving, this brain of a man actually had the audacity to ask me, "Where will I go?"

A few months later, he moved out of his mother's house and rented a room above a residential garage in Franklin, Virginia. He lived there for a while. Then he moved into a brick house in the small town of Capron, Virginia, just ten miles from our house in Southampton County. One of his sisters lived on the outskirts of Capron.

He saw the kids every other weekend.

In the meantime, my father was diagnosed with cancer September 1996. D.L. and I were separated in May of that same year. Daddy regressed rapidly and died December 20, 1996, five days before Christmas. My mother called me Monday evening, December 16, to tell me that Daddy was not in his right mind. She said he was not eating nor resting peacefully. Tuesday, December 17, I took a day off from work and went to Mother's to be with her, as well as observe Daddy's condition. When I got there, everything was pretty much as Mother had told me. Daddy was restless and would not lie down and be still. He kept rising up from the bed, moaning and crying in pain. I could not stand it. I asked Mother to call Dr. Edwards, my father's doctor. He suggested we call the rescue squad, and Mother did so immediately. Upon their arrival, we told them that Daddy was not eating and was mentally unstable, but one gentleman kept insisting that my father was okay and able to eat. I got so angry; I finally shouted out, "My father does not know what he is doing!" I explained that he could not eat on his own, and we could not force him to eat. I told him that my father needed to be in a hospital. After taking his vitals, they put Daddy on a stretcher and took him out to the rescue squad. I climbed in the rescue squad with my father, and we rode to the hospital together. I kidded around with him, saying, "It's kinda bumpy, isn't it, Daddy?"

He grinned and nodded his head, "Yes." That evening, others stayed with him. The next night, my mother and Aunt Bea, my mother's sister-in-law, stayed at the hospital with my father.

On Thursday, December 19, I chose to stay with Mother at the hospital. Daddy had gotten increasingly worse, and our family members were all present for most of the evening. Even D.L.'s sisters, Carolyn and Bee Bee, came to show their support. They loved Daddy. Everyone who knew Daddy loved him. Mama stayed awake as long as she could. Finally, I insisted that she get over on the cot and try to take a little nap. Mama fell asleep, and I sat by Daddy's side all night. Most of the night, I listened for Daddy's breathing every minute. An oxygen bag had been placed over his mouth and nose. The breathing was raspy and coarse.

The next morning, our pastor, Jim Kerr, entered the hospital room at about 7:00 A.M. We talked for a minute, and then I said, "Jim, I don't hear Daddy breathing."

We listened for a minute and then he said, "No, I don't think he is. We better call the nurse. I began to cry and quickly aroused Mother to tell her Daddy had left us. She began to cry helplessly. Our pastor called his wife and my Aunt Bea who both arrived shortly after. I called Mike, my boyfriend, who had been by my side since my father had taken ill. After calling, it seemed as though I had hardly turned around before he was there in the doorway. I had never been so glad to see anyone in my entire life. This tall, brawny, six-foot-five inch man was a welcomed sight. He was a handsome boulder of a man, to say the least, with a strong square jaw, broad shoulders, and sort of messy, sandy hair.

When I saw Mike, I began to cry more intensely, but his big, strong arms held me tightly and he somehow assured me that everything was going to be all right. Edna, another childhood friend of Mother arrived. She and Aunt Bea held mother while Mike consoled me. Jim and his wife, Genie, were also with us until it was time to leave.

After Daddy was pronounced dead, Mike took Mother and me home to Mother's house. Friends and family dropped by for the rest of the day and into the evening. My father only had one sister who had been hospitalized in a nursing home in Chesapeake, Virginia, for a number of years. She was diagnosed with Parkinson's disease; her mind and physical limbs were not intact. Most of Daddy's nieces and nephews came to be with us. D.L.'s mother and father kept Mark and Katie until I could take them home with me. D.L. dropped by the house to offer his condolences. I met him at the door. He was not welcomed in the house because of my father's wishes. Daddy made that fact clear after D.L. and I were separated following my father's diagnosis of cancer. D.L. said he would like to go by and see him if there was no objection. Upon mentioning it to Daddy, he abruptly stated, "No! I did not want him to come in this house before, and he will not come in here now. He will never come into this house again!" Mother had tried to encourage Daddy to change his mind, but he refused. D.L. never took another step in my father's house, even though he did attend the funeral.

My Aunt Bea and I had to go to the funeral home, Saturday evening, December 21, to discuss the arrangements with the funeral director. My mother was very unstable emotionally and wanted the two of us to go. Aunt Bea drove, and so, we indulged in light conversation on the way over to the funeral home. My aunt had left my mother's brother, Ryland Collins Fox Sr.

a number of years prior to his dying of emphysema. She also left behind two small sons, Ryland C. Fox Jr., nicknamed "Jett" after our grandfather, and William Samuel Fox, called "Sam" for short. Sam was named after Dr. Sam Billy Grizzard who delivered him. Jett was only ten and Sam, eight, when their mother left their father, my Uncle Buck, for a younger man. The Fox family was from the "old school." To say the least, we were all devastated at the actions of my Aunt Bea. She left her two small children behind. What kind of mother leaves her children? My mother and her sister and brothers believed in looking out for each other. There were two brothers and two sisters: my Uncle Buck, his brother, Jethro Ward Fox who was the oldest of the four, and the two younger sisters, Virginia, and my mother, Lucille Majorie Fox. My mother was the youngest of the four and spoiled, so they told me. At any rate, since my Aunt Bea left Uncle Buck for what she thought to be her "dream man," a jack of all trades, my mother's family had been very hurt and rejected. Soon, Aunt Bea remarried and became Mrs. Keith Hart. After Mr. Hart began to show his true self, and my aunt became a victim of abuse, she finally kicked him out and threatened to call the law should he return.

Aunt Bea always felt guilty about her past mistakes—leaving Uncle Buck and the boys. This, among other things, is what we talked about on the way to the funeral home. The flashbacks, past memories, all became very real as she poured out her heart to me. Aunt Bea tried to be very heartfelt, announcing to me that she has never forgiven herself for what happened between her and Uncle Buck during our twenty-minute drive. I just sat quietly, in my own deep thought, trying to reassure her as best I could. "I understand, Aunt Bea."

The Burial

Chapter Four

My mother and I withstood the eve of visitation remarkably well. Perhaps it was from being surrounded with warmth and love from my father's nieces and nephews whom we had not seen in years.

Also, my close companion, Mike, stood right behind me throughout the evening. He was almost like a strong pedestal for me to grasp or clutch, as I needed, for support.

Sunday, December 22, 1996, was a day of very little sunshine for my mother, me, and my two children. Grimps was something extra special to his only two grandchildren, Mark and Katie. He loved them to death, and they loved him as much. The biggest grin would sweep across my father's face every time we entered the house. He would always say, "How are my grandchildren?"

They would smile, say, "Fine," and then rush to his arms for a hug. Then my mother would enter the room, and they would say, "Hey, Mimie," and ran to her for another hug.

Along with the bitter cold temperature, the wind was raging. It was the day that most people attending the funeral expected to see Daddy's one and only child crack. His little girl was not supposed to get through this day sanely.

My father and I had a very tight-knit relationship for most of my unmarried life. We could easily engage in a very intellectual conversation about his job as warden of a prison or my college life until the wee hours of the night. Other times, Daddy was a big teaser. He loved to tease me, especially about getting up early in the mornings. He knew I hated it. He would always say, "Come on, Daught. Rise and shine! There's frost on the pumpkin!"

I would just respond, "Oh, Daddy!"

To this day, I recall the moment that we stepped into the funeral home. I honestly believe that my mother wondered if I would break like a small twig being pounded by some wild stallion. The funeral went as well as expected, considering the person who died was not just any father but *my* father! When we arrived at the graveside, everyone was watching and awaiting the moment for my mother and me to exit the vehicle. I felt the stares as we began to make our journey toward the grave. Then it happened; everyone and everything began to move in slow motion. As we walked together, my mother and I clutched each other's arms as we maneuvered our way down the very dark path of death. It did not matter how many family members were with us. Mother and I felt all eyes upon us—mother, me, and my father's only two grandchildren.

Perhaps it was determination and a time to prove everyone wrong, but it looked as though my father's one and only child and his wife, his high school sweetheart surged through the storm and somehow survived it.

As I look back, my heart tells me that I forced myself to be strong. Not only were my father and I close, but there were no two closer humans on this earth as deeply in love than my mother and father. They adored each other. Daddy and Mother were totally devoted to one another. As we walked, I truly believed that my seventy-year-old mother was holding it together for me, as I was for her. We were not going to fall to pieces as everyone anticipated. For this reason, we both held our chins up and heads high, as my father would have wanted us to do. We finally reached the coffin. While the bugle played, Mark and Katie, ages eleven and nine, maintained their composure extremely well. Again, Mike, my companion and my support system, was in many ways also a reassurance to the kids.

Their biological father and my former husband attended the graveside service. He hugged my mother and left rather indiscreetly. He had come by my mother's the day before, met me at the door, hugged me, and told me how sorry he was to hear of Daddy's death. He said he knew how close we were and he just wanted to offer his condolences. I said, "Thank you," and politely closed the door. My father had not wanted D.L. to ever step foot in his house again after our separation.

The graveside service was a military one and was very appropriate for my father—a World War II veteran. It was so cold. We only greeted people for a short time. Then in time it was over.

"The Change"

Chapter Five

Over the next few months, I began to feel more and more comfortable with Mike. He was one of the most compassionate, understanding men I had ever met. Yet, he was firm with his convictions, upon which he had been raised.

We had actually grown up just a few miles from each other, and he and his first wife attended D.L.'s and my wedding. His first wife's older sister, JoAnne, and I were childhood friends. After Mike and JoAnne's younger sister, Sandra, had been married for seventeen years, at thirty-four years of age, she died with a brain tumor. He met someone else a year or so later. However, his second wife had health problems and preferred to drink beer at her mama's all day rather than take her medication and behave responsibly. The marriage ended but for totally different reasons from his first marriage.

Mike's relationship to his second wife ended about the same time D.L.'s and my relationship ended. In October 1996, I was desperate for a companion. D.L. and I had been separated by mutual agreement since May 1996, and in September, Daddy was diagnosed, operated on, and found incurable of his cancerous disease of the lungs. I had talked with a male friend over the phone but had not gone out anywhere in several months. After conversations with my Aunt Bea, I joined her and a friend at a local hot spot called Sue's. An Elvis Presley look-alike was the featured event for the evening of October 5, 1996. I danced with several men, as a result of Aunt Bea's coercion, but little did I know I would end up dancing with the man who is now my husband—David Michael Daniels, better known as "Mike." He had already been made aware of my arrival through conversation with Aunt Bea. He and his coworker, Troy, had been doing carpentry and remodeling on Aunt Bea's house. That night, he was with a few friends, but he had no formal date, and neither did I. One dance led to another, and I was totally mesmerized. Upon leaving, he gave me a good-bye hug, and I told him to give a call sometime.

The following Sunday, the kids and I had been to Mother's for lunch, as we often did on Sundays after church. Upon our return home, there was a message on the answering machine. The voice said, "This is Mike. I just thought I would give you a call…just to talk." I immediately returned the call. We chatted for a while. He asked if I would like to go out sometime, and I said, "Yes."

We received a joint invitation to dinner at my friend, Bootsie's home. At that time, she was dating Mike's business partner, Troy, and so we made a nice "foursome."

From then on, we did things together, just the four of us. Mike and I continued to grow closer in one way but further apart in other ways. We went through stages of me mistrusting him because of experiences I had gone through with D.L., my first husband. Then he finally told me he could not take it anymore. He said it would never work because I did not trust him. I recall him saying, "A relationship is based on trust. If you don't have trust, then you call it quits!"

One night, we had a horrible argument over the telephone. I missed him because we had not seen each other in a couple of weeks. He was yelling, "I told you it's over! I can't live with someone who does not trust me. All we do is argue over where I've been all day, or whom I've seen! I'm tired of it! I told you now it's over!"

I was devastated. I could not imagine my life without him. I kept crying and screaming, "But I love you! I need you! I have no one else!"

He kept shouting, "I told you that's it! You don't love someone and not trust them! It's over! Now hang up!"

I refused to hang up. I kept sobbing like a small child who was being taken away from its mother.

Finally, he agreed to give it one more try. He said he loved me, but he was not going to put up with the mistrust. From that moment on, I knew I had to change.

Eventually, our relationship over the next year began to fall into place. One night, he was over at the house, and he said he wanted to take me out to Applebee's for my birthday the next weekend. I was totally ecstatic! Applebee's in Colonial Heights, Virginia, was my favorite place to go out dining. The steak, fries, beef tips, and salads were the best! And that's not to mention one of my favorite drinks—the famous "Bahama Mama." I liked the drink because it was a mixed drink with a delicious, fruity taste.

The meal was very pleasurable, as I had expected it to be. However, little did I know, the meal was only the beginning. Mike told me he had something for me. He pulled out a nicely-wrapped little box. He said, "When you open it, if you don't like it, or don't want it, let me know and I'll exchange it first for something else." I thought perhaps it was a nice pair of earrings or a dainty necklace.

As I carefully began to unwrap the gift and open the box, I found a small case. Still not sure of what it was, I slowly opened the case and there it was! A tiny, sparkling, diamond—an engagement ring. I cried out, "It's beautiful!"

He stated, "Now, again, if you need more time to think about it, or you don't want it, just say so."

I said, "You know I want it." I took it out of the box and tried it on. It was about a half size too big.

Mike said, "The jewelry store will adjust it to fit as needed." The rest of the evening I really do not recall. I was either in total ecstasy, or sailing smoothly on "Bahama Mamas"; maybe both.

However, I do know, on June 19, 1998, Mike offered me an invitation for marriage, and I said, "Yes!"

We were married at our home on August 8, 1998. It was a small but lovely outdoor wedding. I had asked my hairdresser to decorate because she had a "knack" for arranging flowers and bows. Mike had previously built a deck out from the back of his house, which led straight out to an above ground pool. It was beautiful. Then he had taken the outdoor swing I had bought from my previous house and put it up on one side of the deck, off from the pool.

My favorite wedding picture was the one with the two of us sitting in the swing with magnolias and greenery entwined over and around the two wooden swing posts. It was beautiful. Mike had his arm around me, and you could tell from the low-lying shadows, which surrounded us, that the sun was just beginning to set.

Following that picture, we were walking away from the swing, and all of a sudden, Mike swooped me up in his long, strong arms and tilted me towards the pool. I laughed and screamed, "No, you don't!" Flash! It was another picture…another memory. Mike laughed and gently put me down. We walked away towards the crowd, holding hands.

Blind Fury

Chapter Five

D. L. had begun keeping the children every other weekend since he and I had been formally separated and then divorced. This allowed Mike and me to have some private time of our own. We usually took advantage of it, going out dancing at Sue's place or cooking steaks on the grill with friends, Bootsie and Troy. It was nice; however, I was always so glad to see the children upon their return on Sundays.

D. L. always picked up the children around 6:15 P.M. or 6:30 every other Friday and had them back anywhere between 3:30 and 5:00 P.M. on Sundays.

After Mike and I were married, Katie began showing some resistance on the weekends she was supposed to go to her father's house. She and Mark would come home on Sundays, sometimes smiling, in a good mood, but other times, they were entering the house not saying a word. On the Sundays they entered the house not speaking, I would try and cheerfully ask, "How was your weekend? Did you have a good time?"

At first, they would still say nothing. Then Katie was usually the one to say, "Daddy was fussing all weekend."

Mark would follow by adding, "Yes, he was, Mama."

When I asked, "What was he fussing about?"

One, or the other, would usually say, "About our music being too loud."

That was all they would say at first. Then other times, it would be that he had fussed at Katie because she had dropped something. Once, Katie and Mark came home and told me their Daddy had hit Katie on the head with a video-tape.

D.L. always had a different story. When I questioned him about it, he said, "I did not hit her on the head with it." He said, "I just tapped her on the head with it because she and Mark were arguing over what movie they wanted to watch."

One day in April 2001, I was taking dirty clothes out of the laundry basket in the kid's bathroom. I found three or four pairs of Katie's underwear soiled with blood. Not only were the pairs of underwear heavily stained with blood, they were all bound together as if worn and pulled off at the same time. I could not believe it! My daughter was too young to be starting her menstrual period; she was only eleven years old.

I immediately called Katie. I asked, "Katie, are you bleeding?"

She reluctantly answered, "Yes." Then she began to cry and say, "I'm sorry, Mama."

Katie was not mentally aware of what was happening. I tried to explain to her that she had done nothing wrong. She kept crying, "I'm sorry, Mama! I'm sorry!"

Finally, after a great deal of talking and reassurance, I thought Katie understood that her bleeding was normal. I tried to explain that all young ladies go through this when they are growing up.

She asked, "How long will it last?"

I answered, "It usually lasts about a week."

She interrupted, "Then it will all be over?"

I replied, "It will be over for this month, but then it will happen again next month."

Regaining her composure but still very worried, she said, "Oh, Mom, don't tell me that."

One of Katie's handicapping conditions was absolutely having no concept of time. She could not tell the difference between one week and one month. It all ran together for her. She could not even distinguish between today and two days from now. All she could comprehend was today and tomorrow. At times, this was even vague to her.

The next time their father came to pick them up, I told him that Katie had started her period. He looked down and began shaking his head from side to side as though he could not believe it. But he said nothing.

In the beginning, Katie's menstrual periods went from dark to light. The first month or two, I was convinced Katie's cycle's were finally regular. Then a month might go by and she would have no period at all, or another two months would go by and she would have a period for three weeks each month.

When I questioned Katie about still being on her period, she would sometimes say, "Yes," and other times respond, "No."

I continued to remind her that it was most important that she wear her pads while she was bleeding.

One weekend, she came home from her Daddy's in a bad mood. I found some underwear I had packed for her to take to her Daddy's. There were three or four pairs intermingled again, as if they had all been worn at the same time. Again, they were soiled with the reddish brown substance.

I went to Katie's door and knocked. She said, "Come in."

I began, "Katie, did you start your period again while you were at your Daddy's?"

She answered, "Yes."

I continued, "You didn't have any pads with you, did you?"

"No, Mama."

Then I became furious. "Why didn't your Daddy go and get you some? Did you ask him?"

She shouted, "I told him I didn't have any with me, Mom, but he wouldn't go get me some!"

I was outraged, to say the least. Yet, I was not totally surprised. D. L. had always been selfish, self-centered, and easily embarrassed, even when it came to his own children.

Once, he had gotten up and left the church right in the middle of a Vacation Bible School commencement. Mark's class was performing, and Mark was terrified. He was only about four or five years old. Mark began crying, and D. L. was so angry and embarrassed, he just got up and walked out.

This was typical of his behavior. D. L. could never face his problems; he was always a coward and ran away from them instead.

I began to worry more and more about Katie and her heavy bleeding. Another time, she had come home from her father's house, again with blood-stained underwear. I questioned, "Didn't you have pads with you?" After the one weekend when her father had refused to go out and buy her pads when she needed them, I always made sure she took some every time she went to his house. Her menstrual periods were so irregular and lengthy at times. All of a sudden, she began to cry. I asked, "Katie, what's wrong?"

She said, "Nothing, Mama," But her crying became much more intense.

We were in her room so I gently shoved the door close and insisted Katie tell me what was wrong.

She blurted our sharply, "It's Daddy! He is what made me like this!"

Trying to reassure myself, I further inquired, "What do you mean your Daddy is why you are like this? Do you mean your bleeding, or the dirty pants, or what?"

Still sobbing, she continued as she nodded her head. "I mean all of it Mom! I don't like going to Daddy's!"

Trying to be patient, I replied, "Katie, the bleeding is not your Daddy's fault. That is just what happens to young girls. I mean your Daddy hasn't done anything to you, has he?"

Katie at first nodded her head, "Yes."

I questioned, "Your father has done something to you? What is it? What has he done?"

Perhaps my arousing anger disturbed Katie. She paused for a minute and then she said, "Nothing, Mom."

After continuing to encourage her to say what she wanted to say, she still clammed up, refusing to say anything anymore. It was at this point that I truly began to suspect D.L. was doing something to Katie. I talked to Mike about it. He, too, suspected something. However, we were not absolutely sure, so we preferred not to face the reality of what it might be. Besides, Katie refused to acknowledge or tell us what it was her Daddy had done.

I told D. L. what had happened the next time he came to pick up the children. I even told him that Katie had screamed out that *he* had caused the bleeding. Whenever I approached D. L. about something the kids had come home and told me about him, his first reaction was one of fury. A spark of anger would flash across his face, his eyes would frown, and his lips would form a thin line. Then he would quickly change his expression to one of calm meekness. This time, he did the same. He said, "I don't know why she said that. I have not laid a hand on her. I don't know why she and Mark keep coming home to you and acting like they didn't have a good time. And Katie...why does she make up stories about me?"

I looked at D. L. "I don't know why she said it, but I will be taking her to my gynecologist just as soon we can get an appointment. The bleeding for three weeks at a time has got to stop!"

Luckily, we were able to get appointment within about two weeks. It was early October 2000, and Dr. Smith, my gynecologist, examined her. He stated that he preferred not to pursue an in-depth thorough examination because he did not want to hurt or frighten her.

It was Dr. Smith's recommendation, since Katie was not adjusting well to the change, that perhaps we put her on pills to hopefully regulate her periods. Then we discussed perhaps putting her on the twenty-one-day cycle pill which would simply eliminate her periods completely, since she was young and moderately handicapped. I agreed to try this. He assured me that when she was a bit older, we could take her off of the pill and she would begin her periods as normal.

For the next four to six months, Katie was experiencing frequent mood swings, angry one minute and fairly calm and collective the next. She was also complaining of stomach problems and still spotting. I took her to our family physician, Dr. Adolph Flowers. He set up an appointment with his wife who was a female gynecologist in our local town.

About two weeks later, about the middle of March, we went to see Dr. Delores Flowers. She recommended a totally different direction. She did not like the fact that Katie was not allowed to have periods at all. She felt this was not good for her health. Therefore, she prescribed a birth control packet that clearly showed the days and numbers of the monthly cycle. The pills were colored differently by the week. At the same time, I sought counseling for Katie. I was becoming increasingly concerned about the mood swings and her worried, unhappy attitudes as it neared the time for her weekend visits with her father.

In the meantime, I kept their father informed of the new developments with Katie's menstrual periods and the plans for seeking counseling.

He did not argue the plans for counseling. He only shook his head from side to side when I discussed the birth control measures with him.

During the summer months of 2001, Catlin seemed a little more at ease. Perhaps it was because she was at home with Mark and me. Because of my teaching career, I was fortunate enough to spend the summer months with my children. We thoroughly enjoyed our days of leisure: sleeping late, swimming, and sunning by the pool, or the kids listening to music in their rooms while I pretended to be the "Betty Crocker" of the lawn and garden. Then all of a sudden, reality sets in....back to school for the kids and back to teaching for me.

The Turning Point

Chapter Six

The first month of school in the fall of 2001 went fairly smooth. Katie was twelve years old in the sixth grade because I decided to hold her back a year in fourth grade. She was not progressing in a timely fashion that particular year. Mark was fifteen years old and was in his sophomore year of high school.

Katie and Mark were continuing the overnight visits with their father every other weekend as usual. Katie's mood swings seemed to become more prevalent. We had stopped the counseling over the summer months because everyone seemed calmer or more relaxed. I had planned to seek counseling again for Katie because Katie was beginning to have some problems at school with other students in her special education class.

I taught sixth grade language, arts, and history classes at Belfield Elementary, which was the same school Katie attended as a student. This allowed me to be easily accessible to Katie's teachers if they needed to reach me for any reason. Most of the time, they were very professional and set up after school meetings.

However, the last couple of weeks in October were like a roller coaster ride with Katie. She began having problems on a regular basis, about every two to three days. We had several parent/teacher conferences with Katie present to try and resolve her problems. Because of her constant battle with another young lady, Lati´a, it was decided that Katie would be moved to another homeroom. No more Lati´a, thank God!

Katie's behavior had progressed to a point where she was getting up and leaving the class to go see Mrs. Jones, the guidance counselor, without permission. She had even exhibited some defiant behaviors, talking back to the teacher and sitting in class pouting, instead of doing the assigned work.

The transition from one homeroom to another was a good one. Katie seemed to be somewhat happier and a tad more relaxed.

Unfortunately, the calm did not last very long.

It was the first weekend in November 2001, and it was time for another weekend visit with D. L. The following Monday, Katie was extremely quiet. Katie rode with me to and from school, just as Mark had done when he attended Belfield in the fifth and sixth grades. Katie was sometimes quiet on Monday mornings, but other times, she was rather cheerful. However, no matter what moods she exhibited, she always offered to pass out the morning work for me. The morning work was generally a worksheet for students to complete upon their arrival at school before the first class began at 9:00 A.M.

Katie always enjoyed completing that task because she knew she was being a helper to me in preparing for the day's activities with the students.

That particular Monday morning, however, she entered my classroom and sat down. She did not move. I questioned her about what was wrong. She hesitated and finally said, "Nothing." I asked her if something had happened at her father's that upset her. She continued to sit immobile, with her head hanging, and then said, "No, Mama."

I inquired, "Katie, don't you want to pass out the morning work?"

She paused and responded coolly, "Yea, I'll pass it out, Mama."

I continued gently, "Well, don't you want to? You usually like to help me in the mornings."

She got up, took the morning work out of my hands, and began placing a worksheet on each desk.

By the time she finished, my students were entering. When my students began coming in, it was always a cue for Katie to go to her homeroom. This particular morning was no different from any other.

We had no time to continue the conversation, so Katie said, "Bye, Mom."

I responded, "Bye! See you this afternoon!"

For the next several mornings, Katie continued to exhibit the same shy, guarded behavior. She had very few words to say, and her mind seemed totally preoccupied with something other than what was going on around her. All she did was sit and stare down at the floor in the mornings and afternoons when we were together at school.

Finally, by the fourth day, I knew I had to put the pressure on Katie to talk.

It was Thursday afternoon. Katie entered my room as usual to wait for me to finish up some paperwork before leaving. I greeted her as normal and watched her for a few minutes. I tried to carry on light conversation with her, but, unfortunately, it was to no avail.

Then I charged, "Katie, there is something on your mind! Now, what is it?"

"Nothing, Mom," she answered, refusing to look at me straight in the eye.

Again, I insisted, "Katie, you have not been yourself all week. I can tell something is on your mind. Now, what is it?"

Suddenly, her eyes filled with water, and she softly cried, "Mama, something *is* wrong. I want to know, is Dixie going to die?"

Dixie was the older of our two chocolate Labrador retrievers. She was the mother to Muffin, our youngest lab.

I insisted, "No, Katie. Why do you think Dixie is going to die? She is old, but she is not sick. Why do you think she is going to die? What are you talking about?"

Again, I spoke more forcibly, "Katie, something *is* wrong. Something happened at your Daddy's last weekend, didn't it?"

It was like I had just popped the lid off a tightly sealed jar, or like a dam burst and the water rushed into the river. Katie began to sob more vigorously. She nodded her head up and down.

Then I felt my heart breaking into pieces. I pushed myself to continue, "Katie, what happened? Did your daddy put his hands on you?"

She nodded again, "Yes, Mama."

A knot began rising up in my throat, causing me to hesitate. "What did he do, Katie? Did he touch your private parts?"

She cried again, "Yes, Mama. He did."

I further questioned, "Where? Where else did he touch you? What else did he do?"

"He put his hands all over my breasts, Mama."

"Was it just your breasts? Did he try and put his private parts into your private parts?"

"No, Mama! No. He didn't do that. He just put his hands all over me."

By then, it was almost 5:00 P.M. We were normally at home by that time. I said to Katie, "We have to go home now. It's getting late, but we will continue this conversation at home. We will go home, eat supper, and then talk some more. You have to tell me everything your father did, Katie. Everything!"

We left school. I called Mike on my cell phone and told him something horrible had happened to Katie. I said we were on our way home, and I would tell him about it when we got home. I did mention that it involved the last weekend visit at their father's.

By the time we had gotten home, Mike had started preparing dinner. We both said very little to each other at first. I believe he knew that whatever I had to tell him involved Katie and her father, and it was not good.

Katie and Mark ate supper as usual, around six o'clock. They had taken their baths, and it was about forty-five minutes before their regular bedtime.

I told Katie to come in the master bedroom so we could finish the conversation we had begun at school in privacy. We entered the bedroom and the two of us sat down on the side of the bed.

I said, "Katie, we are going to finish the conversation we started at school, and you have to tell me everything! Everything your father did, you must tell me!"

She began to sob, "You know what you asked me at school about Daddy putting his private parts in mine? Well, he did, Mama! He did!"

My stomach began to churn, and my heart sank. I, too, began sobbing as I grabbed Katie. We both held on to each other tightly as the flood of tears continued.

Upon further questioning, I came to know that not only did her father rape her more than once, he also sodomized her.

I was unable to sleep that night as many other nights to come.

Katie already had a scheduled appointment with our family physician, Dr. Adolph Flowers the next day, for the purpose of getting a refill on the adderall, which is a time-release medication usually prescribed to children and young adults who have been diagnosed with attention deficit disorder. Many doctors require a three-month visit before continuing refills on the medicine. Katie had also been experiencing some insomnia, and so, the visit was a much needed and welcomed one. I chose to take this opportunity to request that Dr. Flowers do a pelvic examination on Katie to determine if there was physical evidence of damage done by her father.

Dr. Flowers was very reluctant to do so because he was very concerned about Katie's temperament and how she would feel about another man exploring her female organs following the recent episode with her father. He insisted that Katie and I talk it over first. He even suggested a local female gynecologist who happened to be his wife to perform the examination. I explained, first, to Katie, and then to Dr. Flowers, that we could postpone the examination for another day, with another doctor, but then, Katie and I would find ourselves in another waiting room, experiencing the same agony, frustration, and anxiousness that we had experienced this particular day. Why not go ahead and get it over with now? In addition, it was of great urgency and importance that we find out what damage, if any, had been done to Katie internally. She was still having heavy bleeding with her menstrual periods, and so it was on the day of this appointment.

Once Dr. Flowers realized I was not going to resign to seeing another doctor, he began to prepare Katie for the pelvic exam. The second time my heart fell to the floor was when Dr. Flowers began gently examining Katie and small subtle tears began to flow down her cheeks. She tried to be strong, showing no weakness, but then she cried out, "Dr. Flowers, please don't hurt me like my daddy hurt me!"

The doctor, nurse, and myself all felt the same sense of helplessness. There was absolutely nothing the three of us could do to take away the pain and agony Katie had gone through and would inevitably continue to go through because of the sick, monstrous acts that her father had performed on her.

Once the examination was over, Dr. Flowers asked to speak to me outside of the patient room. He told me he really could not clearly examine Katie the way she needed to be examined because of her heavy bleeding and his lack of precise equipment. He also asked me what my intentions were. I asked, "What do you mean, Dr. Flowers? You heard her. I most certainly plan to take legal action!"

He responded, "Well, do you plan to seek your own private attorney, or have us make contact with Child Protective Services?"

I answered, "Either way, I will definitely be contacting a lawyer."

He then turned and walked away. I reentered the room where Katie was patiently waiting.

She asked, "What are we going to do now, Mom?"

I replied, "I don't know, Katie. The examination is over, and we will just wait and see what Dr. Flowers says for us to do."

A few minutes later, the nurse came in and told me that Katie and I would have to remain at the doctor's office a while longer; Dr. Flowers had contacted the Child Protective Services and we had to await their arrival before leaving. She stated they would probably want to interview me and Katie. I said, "Fine. We'll wait."

Approximately thirty minutes later, Mr. Michael Hinton from the local Social Services Department arrived and asked to speak to me. We went into the examination room that was not being used. I had Katie to wait in a small waiting area out in the hall. He proceeded to tell me he was not going to interview Katie that day because he realized she had already been through an ordeal with the examination. He said he wanted to speak to me for just a few minutes and, at the first of the next week, a couple of agents from Social Services would probably be coming out to the school to talk with Katie and myself. I had no problem with this whatsoever.

Mr. Hinton began asking questions about what lead us to the doctor's office and what had Katie told me. I gave him every ugly detail as she had given it to me the day before. He informed me that he would probably be contacting the sheriff's department upon his return to the office and there was a good chance that a deputy would be visiting us, either at home or school, in the next couple of days.

Sure enough, that following Tuesday after Katie's examination on Friday, we were called down to the office, individually, for interviews with the Greensville County Social Services Department representatives.

They called me down at about 10:30 or 11:00 A.M. That morning, I was unaware of the fact that they had already interviewed Katie when I entered. Upon my inquiry, they explained that they had already spoken with Katie. The two counselors included a White male, perhaps in his early fifties, and a Black female, probably in her early to mid-thirties. They simply asked me to recount, as best I could, exactly what Katie had reported to me.

The interview lasted approximately twenty-five or thirty minutes. I questioned what would happen next. They stated that someone from the Social Services Department would be contacting me in the next couple of weeks to explain what procedures were being taken.

In the meantime, Dr. Flowers had made an appointment with a female pediatric gynecology practitioner at the world-renowned Medical College of Virginia (MCV). He had told us about the appointment prior to our leaving his office on Friday.

Dr. Flowers explained that the specialist, Beverly Liles, was excellent in cases of suspected child molestation and abuse.

Approximately one week later, Katie and I had taken off a day of school to attend the MCV appointment scheduled for 9:30 A.M. We were just preparing to walk out the door at about 7:45 A.M. when I received a call from MCV. The appointment was going to have to be rescheduled. The gynecology practitioner was going to be absent from work that day.

Katie and I were a little agitated because we both wanted to get the examination behind us. I made it my priority to always explain to her, at length, what was going to happen, so she would not be caught off guard. Because we were both dressed for the doctor's visit and somewhat emotionally drained from everything that had been going on, I decided that Katie and I would just stay home for the day and get some rest.

The following week, we once again prepared for the trip to MCV. Once we arrived, we were sent to a small waiting room that seated maybe four to six patients. The practitioner asked to speak to me first. She explained that she would interview me first then interview Katie and, lastly, proceed with the examination.

We went into her office. She began asking questions. As I started to speak, recalling the same gory details as I had been asked to do several times before, my eyes began to fill with tears. I quickly tried to regain my composure, knowing that Katie was waiting alone out in the waiting room. She normally did not cater to being left alone, or thrown in a room full of strangers without me being nearby.

At the conclusion of my interview, the practitioner's assistant escorted me back to the waiting room and politely motioned for Katie to go with her. Katie did so with no resistance.

After a long forty-five minutes, the practitioner's assistant came to the waiting room and told me they needed me in the office. As we walked, she explained that Katie was fine, but she had gotten somewhat emotional while revealing the details of what her father had done to her.

Upon entering the office, I saw that Katie was seated, crying in a strong voice, holding out her arms to me, and muttering, "Mama, I'm sorry. I couldn't help crying. I got upset when I was telling what Daddy did to me."

I walked over and wrapped my arms around her tightly, saying "Katie, it's all right. It's okay to cry. You have a right to be upset. I got upset, too, when I had to talk about what your father had done!"

The practitioner motioned to me that she and her assistant were stepping out for a few minutes to give us time alone. I nodded my head in confirmation of the much-needed break.

After a few minutes, both reentered. The practitioner asked Katie which stuffed animal among all of those lined up and down the walls she liked.

Katie chose a cute little stuffed rabbit. Actually, it was a pair: boy and girl. Katie chose one of the two.

The practitioner handed Katie the one she had chosen. Then she smiled and added, "You can have them both, if you like!"

Katie was tickled to death. She grabbed both rabbits in her arms and said, "Look, Mom! I get to have both of them!"

I grinned, grateful of the practitioner's sense of compassion for her patients.

Then came the probing moment. Katie had to remove the lower part of her clothing, from the waist down. She climbed up on the table as directed and prepared for the forthcoming discomfort.

The practitioner picked up a cotton swab and explained to Katie each step of what she was preparing to do. She asked me to stand at the head of the table, and I quickly took my place. Then a large brown cabinet next to the examination table was opened. I was not in a position to see what was in the cabinet. However, as she began probing gently, she kept a constant watch on whatever was in the cabinet. My common sense led me to know that it was some type of video equipment that took pictures of whatever she was observing during the test. Periodically, she would remark to her assistant, "There's one. Do you see it? Let's get that one."

After a short time, it was over. Beverly Liles instructed Katie to get her clothes back on while she and her assistant stepped out.

They returned after a few minutes. Beverly hugged Katie and told her she was a brave little girl. She continued to tell Katie that she had done exactly right by telling someone what had happened.

Katie gave her another hug. The practitioner seemed to be bidding us farewell when I spoke up. "Dr. Liles, you didn't say, but did you not find something or you cannot tell me what you saw?"

She replied meekly, "There were one or two tears that would indicate some forced entry."

She continued, "I will be sending copies of everything I have to your local social services department. The police department will also receive copies." She added, "In our conversation, you didn't mention anything about the police. They have been contacted, haven't they?"

I answered timidly, "I really don't know. I was told that a deputy would be visiting us to get a statement, but we have not seen one yet."

In a seemingly shocked manner, she responded, "They should have been contacted by someone long before now!"

A couple of weeks went by. I heard nothing from the police or social services. Finally, moving into the third week, Jessica Thomas called. She stated that she needed to set up a short meeting with me again at her office. There were some specific dates and times of doctor's visits that she needed, as well as a few other details.

The following week, we met. Jessica asked me if she could tape some of the conversation dealing with specific dates, times, and a few details about what Katie had reported to me. I responded that it would be fine.

I questioned Jessica about why, after several weeks, we had not been con-tacted or interviewed by any law enforcement officer. She explained that since the criminal act supposedly occurred in another county, being the father's res-idence, Greensville County was no longer in charge of the case.

The Undeniable Truth

Chapter Seven

The Social Services Department of Southampton County had been contacted by Greensville County and any further action would have to be taken by officials in that county.

Another couple of weeks went by, and still, there was no word from Southampton County. My husband and I were becoming very anxious to say the least. Katie was beginning to open up more and more since she no longer had to go to her father's house.

Since the day at the doctor's office, when social services became involved, Mr. Hinton from social services assured me that neither one of my children had to return to their father's as long as the charges were being brought against him.

At least once every two weeks, Katie would come into the kitchen where I was and say, "Mama, can I tell you something else that happened when we were at Daddy's?"

I would always take a deep breath, in the midst of trying to keep my sanity, and respond "Yes, Katie."

No matter what I was in the middle of doing, if she wanted to talk to me, I listened. Usually, whatever she had to tell me was absolutely devastating, and we would both end up in tears. Sometimes, I just could not take the overwhelming sensation of helplessness and guilt that came over me when she talked about specific nights and details of what her father made her do. I would have to say to her, "Katie, go and tell Mike what you just told me." When she walked out of the room, which was usually the kitchen, I would just sit down and sob uncontrollably. Mike would either sit and hold Katie while she sobbed or, sometimes, just come and hold me and verbally try to comfort Katie at the same time. If it had not been for my husband's compassion and sensitivity, my children and I wouldn't have made it through the entire ordeal, from start to finish.

He, nor I, ever doubted Katie's stories about the abuse. After all, why would a twelve-year-old female wear three or five pairs of underpants and the same number of socks? I had no idea that she was doing this until we made the visits to the doctors. I witnessed the pairs of underwear wrapped up together and the four or five pairs of socks intermingled on the floor following each examination. It was heartbreaking. I typically assumed that her sense of needing to cover up body parts was because of the abuse. The mental and emotional need for protecting and securing herself from her father's intrusion into her body was my theory. But the socks…why all the socks? Finally, she confessed to me one evening that she wore the socks because she wanted to cover her feet. Her father would always rub his feet up against hers during his insane moments of intrusion and molestation.

Katie never slept without a bra on since she was old enough to wear one. I tried to explain to Katie that girls did not usually wear their bras when going to sleep at night because they were hot and uncomfortable. To this day, she still wears a bra twenty-four hours a day. She told me one day that she wanted to keep the bra on.

"I don't want to sleep without it on because it reminds me of Daddy putting his hands all over me!"

Justice, or Not

Chapter Eight

It was February 2002 before I finally received a call from the Southampton County Sheriff's Department. It was a female deputy who requested a day and time that she could come and talk to Katie.

As it happened, she made several visits to our home. She interviewed Katie for at least two hours on one visit and another hour or two on another visit.

Mike, Mark, and I were also interviewed on other dates. Robbie Lynn, the deputy, usually ended up staying anywhere from one and one half to two hours when she came to get statements and details.

Eventually, my family came to acquire a certain rapport with Robbie Lynn. She was there for us, as we were for her when information or concerns arose.

Following the final interview at our home with Robbie Lynn, she told me that the Commonwealth Attorney's Office would probably be contacting us soon. I asked Robbie Lynn if D.L. was going to be arrested and what was happening next.

She made it perfectly clear that he was going to be given a lie detector test, and then we would see what procedures would be taken.

In about a week, late one afternoon, I received a call at work. It was Cora Hawkins, of the Victim/Witness Protection Program. She worked closely with Mr. Edwards, Assistant Commonwealth's Attorney and was calling to schedule the appointment.

The first meeting was rather long, as were the next few. Mr. Edwards would always start off the conversation discussing his latest incidents with his horses. He broke wild horses as a hobby. He seemed to enjoy his outdoor life with his livestock. Katie would usually smile and listen as he talked about his exciting adventures.

As Mr. Edwards began to question Katie during the first meeting, I was allowed to sit in on his interrogation. She did not hesitate to unfold the same traumatizing story as she had done for Robbie Lynn and the doctors. When she began to recount the details, I sat and listened and suddenly the warm teardrops slowly trickled down my cheeks. Cora quickly snatched a tissue from the tissue box and passed it to me with a glancing expression of concern..

Cora always sat in on the meetings because that was her job. She was a major witness to what whatever insanely words passed from the mouths of victims who had been abused as they described the horror scenes inflicted upon them.

At the conclusion of Katie's deposition, the assistant Commonwealth's Attorney stated that he would be taking the case. He said he would talk no further at that time. Katie needed to regain her composure. Cora would be calling and setting up another appointment in a few weeks.

We departed, only to return home where I relayed all of the details of our first meeting. My mother asked that I call her as well.

Periodically, Robbie Lynn called to check on everyone, asking about how the kids were doing. We even met with her a couple of times following the first visit with Mr. Edwards. The kids seemed to develop a close bond with her. Perhaps it was a sense of safeness and trusting that she offered them. Over the course of the time, she had obtained statements from Mike, Mark, and myself. Not once, in all of my many questions to Mark, nor in his statement to Robbie Lyrm, did he ever admit to any physical, or sexual abuse by his father. He did state that his father had a very bad temper. He would get mad at Katie if she dropped and broke something, or scold Mark if he did not clean off the kitchen counters, or sweep the floors to his standards.

Finally, we received another phone call from Cora. Another appointment was scheduled and this time, Mr. Edwards would be discussing the details of what to expect at the Preliminary Hearing in April. He also asked to see Mark. Previously, Mark had confessed that he was not aware of all the events that occurred with his father and Katie. He did recall once hearing Katie calling out for him. Mark stated that he did not go in the bedroom and help his sister for fear of what his father would do. That was all Mark would say.

When the three of us arrived, Mr. Edwards spoke with Mark alone. Then he talked to all three of us. When I questioned about the actions that would be taken at the preliminary hearing, Mr. Edwards stated that Katie would have to recount the events of what her father did to her before the judge, her father and his attorney. He continued to say that he would be the one to question Katie. I would also be interviewed about specific dates and times, but then I would have to leave. Nonetheless, he stated that he and Cora would be there with Katie.

We left his office to go to the judge's chambers. Mr. Edward proceeded to explain to Katie where the preliminary hearing would take place and answer any questions she may have. After briefing us on where everyone would sit and some of the basic procedures, Mr. Edwards asked Katie if she had any questions. She showed hesitancy as she tried to speak.

"What is it Katie?" Mr. Edwards continued. "Don't be afraid to ask. What is it honey?"

Katie slowly and reluctantly responded, "My daddy…he may get mad at me."

Mr. Edwards assuringly answered, "Katie, you know what? I'm going to be sitting right beside you. Your Daddy will be sitting over there." He pointed to the opposite side of the table.

"I don't know how exactly your Daddy looks, but from what I gather, he is not very big. I think I could whip him." We chuckled. He continued, "And you know what else? We have Josh. He is a big man, and he is what we call a 'bailiff'. If your daddy, or anyone gets angry and tries to come towards you, Josh will stop him. That's why he is here…To prevent anyone from getting out of control."

The conversation ended shortly after. Mr. Edwards told Mark that he might want to speak to him again another time, but he would not have to attend the preliminary, hearing.

The Preliminary Trial

Chapter Nine

Mike and I had already planned to go to the preliminary trial. We decided it was best to let Mark stay in school so as not to interrupt his daily routine.

In the meantime, my seventy-five-year-old mother offered that she wanted to attend the preliminary hearing. Quite naturally, I told her that she could ride with Mike, Katie, and me.

Forgetting that my mother was partially deaf, she nearly got us thrown out of the courtroom. Mother had always been very outspoken. The first time, Josh, the bailiff, spoke to us was when my mother saw D.L. and his parade of supporters marching in the courtroom and seating themselves on the front row. D.L., his long-time secret lover, his two sisters, one brother-in-law, and, finally, a very close friend of his and mine filed in with the rest of his "flock." Not only did my best friend and her husband show up on behalf of D.L., but their twenty-year-old daughter also came straggling in behind them.

Katie immediately began to get upset when she saw her father enter the courtroom. She began to get fidgety and almost cry. I looked straight at her and said, "Katie, you are not going to get upset. I know you do not like seeing your father, but you have to be strong. If you want your father to be punished, you have to do this. We will get through it. Do you hear me?"

She answered meekly, "Yes, Mama. I'll be strong." Suddenly, Josh, the bailiff, came over and told us that we must be quiet.

Court was called into session. My mother went absolutely bonkers when she realized that our friends, Lynn, Travis, and their daughter, Amy, were with D.L.'s family.

She turned to me and squealed, "Lynn Ramsey! Is that Lynn Ramsey?" Loudly, the bailiff announced, "You will have to be quiet or be removed from the courtroom!"

I then nodded my head, "Yes, Mama."
I tried to motion my mother, "Sh-h-h!"
She said, "What?"
I tried to whisper, "Mama, be quiet. We have to be quiet. Court has started." She quieted down for the moment.

Other cases were introduced before our case. Finally, the court announced: "Dallas L. Phillips versus the Commonwealth of Virginia." The Black female judge stood and announced that the hearing would be held in the judge's chambers due to the delicateness of the case. She also stated that the case would be completed, and they would return to the courtroom again shortly.

I was called back to the chambers along with D.L. and his attorney. The hearing began with Mr. Edwards asking me a few questions about specific dates and times. Then Mr. Taylor Williams, D.L.'s attorney, asked a couple of questions about the first doctor's examination with Dr. Flowers. The questions were concerned with what led me to take Katie to the doctor and what was Dr. Flowers' diagnosis or findings. I explained that he was unable to make a successful or thorough examination due to Katie's profuse bleeding. I also mentioned that because of this, he referred us to a special practitioner in pediatric gynecology at MCV.

At that point, I was excused, and it was Katie's turn to enter. We passed by each other in the small hallway separating the chambers from the courtroom. I saw the questioning fear in her eyes.

"Katie, it's okay," I reminded. "Be strong. You have to do this. Everything is all right." I tried to speak in a firm but calm voice for her benefit.

She nodded her head "I know, Mama." Bang! The door shut behind them. I felt a sudden sharp sickness in the pit of my stomach as well as a strong sense of uncertainty. I knew Katie was safe, but I also knew her father was insane. I wanted to be with her, to squeeze her hand and tell her it was going to be okay.

My mind was quickly drawn to another scene, a different mood, as I entered the courtroom. I sensed the strong glares as I passed the front row where D.L.'s family and our friends sat. Something from within me, God or my childhood faith, allowed me to keep my head held high, my chin straight, and walk right past them without the blink of an eye. Besides, neither my child, nor I, had done any wrong. D.L. was the low-life, the scum of the earth who had hurt my child.

The next forty-five to fifty-five minutes were the longest in all of my life. Everyone seated in the courtroom felt the tension between his family and mine. Of course, it was only just the three of us versus the eight of them.

Finally, the door burst open. Cora and Katie were the first to exit the judge's chambers. One or two others came out and then D.L. and his lawyer. D.L. was shaking his head from side to side, his eyes glossy and wet with tears. I heard him cry out to his girlfriend and family, "It's not good! It's not good!"

In the meantime, Cora escorted Katie over to us and exclaimed, "It went well! Katie did a very good job!"

I responded, "So what about the judge's decision?"

Cora answered, "She found reason to believe that the case should be taken to a higher court."

All I could think was, *Thank God! This criminal is going to prison!* About this time, Mr. Edwards, Assistant Commonwealth's Attorney, walked over and told me that he would like to see Katie and me in his office for just a few minutes.

We all exited the courtroom. While Katie and I went into Mr. Edwards' office, Mike and Mother waited outside in the hall. Mr. Edwards was extremely pleased with Katie and equally pleased with the judge's decision. Then, the harsh reality came. Their father was going to trial. He was being charged with a felony of child molestation. We would be notified of the trial date in the near future.

Misconception

Chapter Ten

About two weeks had passed when we got the call that the trial date had been set for August 3. Cora called and explained that Mr. Edwards wanted to set up a meeting to review facts and details. She said he also wanted us to come in and observe court one day. This would help to alleviate further questions or concerns that Katie may have about what goes on in circuit court during a trial.

Before our next visit with Mr. Edwards, I had stressed to the children, "If there is anything that you have not told, you need to make sure you say this before the trial."

The night before one of our final meetings with Mr. Edwards, Katie came and told me that her Daddy had done something to Mark, too, but he did not want anyone to know. At this point, Mike and I called both Katie and Mark into the family room. We explained that the truth must be told by both of them, no matter how uncomfortable or humiliating it might be. I stressed over and over to my two children, "Your father must be punished for what he did to one or both of you. You have to speak up and tell every horrid detail of what he did, or he will get off. He will be a 'free' man."

I even spoke directly to Mark. "Son, if there is anything that you have not told us about something that your father did to you, or even if he did the same thing to you that he did to Katie, you must speak up! Otherwise, your father will get off!"

I firmly remarked, "Do you understand?"

He meekly replied, "Yes, Mama."

That night, Mark never opened up, or chose to share any information with Mike or me. The next morning, on the way to the Commonwealth Attorney's Office, I reminded Mark and Katie once more, "Remember: This is it! If you know of anything else that your father did to either one of you, I expect you both to be honest and truthful. You have to tell the truth, always!"

They both nodded their heads, Mark in the front and Katie in the back-seat, "Okay, Mama."

When we arrived at Mr. Edwards' office, he invited all three of us to come in as usual. Cora gathered up chairs for seating the three of us and she also sat, sometimes stood, depending upon the availability of the chairs outside the office.

Mr. Edwards began his meeting as usual, talking about his horses. He had told us, since one of our first meetings, that he had a farm ranch with all kinds of livestock. The horses seemed to be his biggest challenge. He bought wild horses and tamed them. He always told Katie a different story or another major event that had occurred with one of his horses since our last meeting. Katie did not appear to be extremely interested in his horse stories, but she would grin and nod her head acceptingly whenever he began to talk about his horses.

Following his casual conversation, he would then begin the serious talk with one or both of my children. Today, he began reminding them about the importance of telling the truth and the whole truth at all times.

Katie then blurted out.

"Mark has something to tell you."

Mr. Edwards' eyebrows mused and looking surprised, responded, "What? What did you say, Katie?"

She repeated, "Mark has something to tell about what Daddy did to him but he didn't want anyone to know about."

With all eyes looking dead set on Mark, Mr. Edwards began, "Mark? Is there something that you haven't told us about what your father did to you?"

Before Mark could answer, Katie interrupted, "Yep. Tell them Mark. Tell them what Daddy did to you. Tell them what you told me!"

There was a long silence. Then Mr. Edwards repeated his question to Mark. "Mark, son, you must tell the truth. Did your father, in any form or fashion, sexually abuse you like he did to Katie?" Another minute or two passed. Again, there were two minutes which seemed to be like an eternity, and then, the inconceivable unfolded before my eyes.

My son, Mark, began nodding his head up and down, and in a very soft voice answered, "Yes."

My head began whirling. *No! This could not be happening! My ex-husband, perverted and insane, raped my daughter, not my sixteen year old son!* Mark had been denying any sexual assaults all along. This was the first time he had ever admitted any sexual misconduct by his father.

Mr. Edwards was equally surprised. He also suggested we call it a day and allow everyone to regain our composure. He told Mark that Deputy Neaves would be visiting him soon for a statement.

Again, we were told that we would probably be coming for possibly one or two more meetings before the trial date.

The Trial

Chapter Eleven

It was about the end of June and on the first week of July, that we were notified of the trial date.

Cora called to give me a tentative date—August 2. She said she would send me a follow-up memo to confirm this date. Sure enough, in about a week, we received a memo from Cora. Shortly after, subpoenas were issued to Mark, Katie, and me.

In the meantime, Deputy Neaves also made a visit out to the house to get a statement from Mark.

About two weeks before the trial, we were called in to the Assistant Commonwealth Attorney's office again. This time, Mr. Edwards took us through a mock trial session. He even asked the other Assistant Commonwealth Attorney to serve as the defense lawyer to ask us questions that might be offered during the trial.

All in all, the mock trial session went fairly well. Mark had to be reminded to speak up. Katie did extremely well. Mr. Edwards had assured Katie and Mark that Cora would be seated right behind them if they wanted her to. Katie was also concerned about whether or not Josh, the bailiff, would be there.

Mr. Edwards reassured her that Josh would be just a few feet away from her. He told her that no one was going to hurt her.

During the preliminary hearing, D.L. had begun to rock his chair back and forth, smiling and gritting his teeth, while Katie revealed what he had done to her. He moved around so much that Josh had to tell him more than once, "Be still, Sir!" This was what Cora had reported to me.

Prior to the mock trial session in the courtroom, Mr. Edwards had spoken with us to tell us that Mark would not be asked to reveal what his father had done to him at that trial. He also suggested the possibility that it might not be in the best interest of the children for us to go back to court with Mark's accusations after he had denied it for so many months. Perhaps because of my puzzling look of *Why not?* he finally agreed to discuss the situation with Mr. Richard Grizzard, the Commonwealth's Attorney. He stated that he would probably be calling me back in for a meeting sometime after the second trial to give me his final answer.

About four days before the trial, I received a telephone call from my mother. It was to tell me that D.L.'s mother, Katie and Mark's paternal grand-mother, Mrs. Shirley Phillips, ("Nanar)" had passed away. I was sorry to hear of her death for more reasons than one. First of all, Mrs. Phillips had been good to the children even after D.L.'s and my divorce. His family had always been very supportive of me and the children while we were married. More recently, they never seemed to accept D.L.'s adulterous behavior which caused the marriage to end, nor the charge of sexual abuse.

D.L., nor his sisters, had spoken to the children since the charges were brought against him. Mr. and Mrs. Phillips had seen that the children received their annual Christmas monetary gifts, but that was all.

I truly believe that Mrs. Phillips did not want to live to see the trial. I am sure that the entire ordeal was much too strenuous, mentally and physically, for her.

The timing for us, however, was totally off. We had been waiting months for this trial. At that time, I was certain that it would be postponed, and there would be more waiting—long hours, long days.

Sure enough, I received a call, within the next couple of days that the trial was postponed. We could be notified of the new date soon as it was determined by the court.

Unfortunately, we had planned our vacation for August 10 to 17. It was planned purposely after the trial so that the four of us could rest and relax at the beach following the entire ordeal.

About a week before we left on vacation, Mr. Edwards called to tell us the trial date had been rescheduled for August 28, 2002. This was supposed to be the opening convocation date for all teachers returning for the 2002 to 2003 school year; new and veteran teachers must attend. I would have to miss my first day back at work. However, most veteran teachers usually dreaded this particular day. It was very repetitious and took up one-half of a workday that could have been used working in our classrooms. We had classrooms to clean, bulletin boards to put up, and lesson plans to develop. This is not including checking student folders. Every year, each teacher got a new class of students and with them came a new set of folders. We had items to check in the folders before they arrived at school the first day.

At any rate, the next long week passed, and it was time to pack up for the beach. We had rented a cottage close enough to the beach that we could walk from the cottage down to the ocean. We had a beautiful, peaceful vacation on the Atlantic Ocean for one week. It was so pleasant that we all hated to leave and go back home. Of course, the four of us knew what we faced when we got back home—the trial; it was just a few days away.

Finally, August 28 arrived. Our closest friends, Bootsie and Troy, made arrangements to attend. That time, my mother chose not to go. She said that her doctor thought it best she did not go, and I agreed.

We arrived at the courthouse at approximately 8:15 A.M., just as we were told to do so. Mike had to leave us, and go to the courtroom. We were directed to the Witness #1 room. D.L.'s fifteen-character witnesses were in the Witness #2 room next door.

Dr. Flowers, our family physician, Jill Jordan, Katie's counselor, and the practitioner from MCV were all called in to testify on behalf of Katie. Then, Deputy Neaves, Mark, Katie, and I had to testify.

Dr. Flowers, the MCV practitioner, Katie, and her counselor all testified first. Mark and the deputies testified next. I was the last to testify prior to D.L. He had agreed to get on the stand and present his glorified version of the story.

I heard some of it, but I only knew what was told to me by Mike, our friends, and the Assistant Commonwealth's Attorney, Mr. Edwards. I wished I had been allowed to observe.

Unfortunately, D.L. had rounded up so many character witnesses, most who worked with him, that the trial had to go into a second day. I found it interesting his best friend had to leave on a family emergency the first day of the trial. He never returned to testify for D.L.

Katie had done well on the stand. In the beginning, Katie caused a few heartbeats to skip because she refused to talk. When Mr. Edwards asked what was wrong, she remarked, "You promised me Josh was going to be here with me." Mr. Edwards quickly recalled his promise to Katie, and the court came to a brief halt until Josh, the bailiff, was located. Once he took his place up at the front of the courtroom near Katie, she spoke freely and answered questions by both the Assistant Commonwealth's Attorney and D.L.'s attorney, Mr. Williams.

Again, I was told by others what happened; I was unable to observe any of it for myself.

Unfortunately, Mark did not appear as calm and assured as Katie once he got on the stand. First of all, he forgot that he was not allowed to take anything with him once he went into the courtroom to get on the stand. Mark always took his notebook with him when he went to visit Mr. Edwards. He would always type up his notes in his computer and print copies for Mr. Edwards. It seemed easier for Mark to communicate what happened in this fashion rather than blurting it out verbally; he was used to it. He just held on to it for security.

At any rate, Mark walked out of the witness room and into the courtroom with his notebook. He had to give it up. I think it threw Mark completely for a loop when the notebook had to be removed from his hands. I was told that Mark performed okay, but he did appear a bit nervous. I was told that he kept looking over at his father whenever he was asked a question. His father kept shaking his head from side to side. Mark could have easily been intimidated by his father. He was never really close to D.L. You might say, he was even afraid of him.

Finally, near the end of the first day, I was called out to testify. I was calm but probably not as dramatic as I should have been. The questions were to the point and very few. My answers were to the point, with no elaboration. I have often thought, since then, that I should have taken the bull by the horns and thrown out many more details; there were so many things that I would do differently if I had another chance.

Nonetheless, there was one incident which occurred while I was on the stand that I would never change.

When the two counselors finished questioning me, which took very little time, I looked straight at that animal of a man, and I did what I had wanted to do for a long time. It was perfect. Both counselors were looking down at their notes, and as I rose to leave the stand, I looked at him dead in the eye and whispered, "You son of a bitch!" He quickly got his counselor's attention and began pointing to me. I walked right past the two of them, out of the courtroom, and back to Witness #1 room.

Then came the rebuttal. The intercom in Witness #1 room came on.

A voice said, "Mrs. Sharon Daniels, please return to the courtroom. Sharon Daniels."

I got up and walked out of the witness room and down the hall to the courtroom. I entered the courtroom and took my place back on the stand.

"Mrs. Daniels, as you were getting ready to leave the courtroom, did you mouth something to Mr. Phillips?" questioned D.L.'s attorney.

I answered, "Yes."

"Mrs. Daniels," the judge continued, "would you please repeat what you said to Mr. Phillips as you were leaving the courtroom?"

I answered coldly, "I called him a son of a bitch."

At this point, Mr. Williams spoke to the judge, saying something about inappropriate courtroom behavior. Judge Westbrook asked Mr. Edwards if he had seen me mouth the words. Mr. Edwards spoke up and said that he had not seen me use profanity towards Mr. Phillips, but under the circumstances, he could certainly understand the anger that Mrs. Daniels, as a mother, might feel towards Mr. Phillips. Both counselors admitted that they did not see me say the words to D.L. The judge did not see me mouth the words, so I was allowed to leave with no further adieu.

The late afternoon and evening went by rather slowly. During the next morning in court, the couple of hours even went by more slowly.

Finally, at about 10:30 A.M., we were called out of the witness rooms to enter the courtroom for the judge's verdict.

We all sat on the edges of our seats: D.L awaiting a decision that could cost him time in prison, his family waiting for either a life of shame or a life of questioning relief, and myself, my two children, and my husband looking for justice to be done. Before the judge began to speak, every moment that passed felt like eternity. Like when Daddy died, everything changed into slow motion.

Our friends were sitting in the row next to us. They were anxiously awaiting an answer, a verdict. We all knew, in the end, "right prevailed over wrong." Mark, Katie, and I had waited so many agonizing months for this moment.

The two attorneys presented their defense statements. I felt Mr. Williams offered stronger arguments, but Mr. Edwards seemed to be too sure that he had the case "nipped in the bud" as the saying goes.

The judge spoke, "After hearing the testimonies of all those involved, there is evidence, and no doubt in my mind, that something has been done to Katie. However, there were too many corroborating statements and questions by the two counselors to the children. Therefore, I have decided to dismiss the charges against Mr. Phillips."

I felt the wind had just been knocked out of me. My husband stood in awe, and so did everyone else in the courtroom, with the exception of D.L. and his loving family. They began jumping up and down, crying for joy, and so was he. Mr. Edwards, Cora, and the deputies involved all hung their heads in disbelief.

In the meantime, Katie was busy asking, "What happened, Mama? Will they take Daddy away in chains now, Mama? Is it all over?"

I quietly told her "No, Katie. We lost the case. Your daddy is off. He is a free man. I do not know why, Katie, but he is."

The rest of the day was sort of a 'blur.' After I got the news to Mother, she too, responded in disbelief and anger. The next call was to Jane Lee, my school principal. She was very much aware of the situation because Katie was attending Belfield Elementary where I worked. Her first words when I told her we lost the case were, "Oh Sharon, I am sorry. I cannot begin to imagine how you must feel. I will keep you in my prayers."

I thanked Mrs. Lee for her concern and hung up the phone. Bootsie, Troy, Mike, and I poured us a moderately stiff drink and sat around staring at the walls, trying to sort out all that had happened the last two days. It was a nightmare. Katie and Mark were very quiet and reserved. They retired to their rooms for the rest of the day until meal time. We were all in a state of awe for quite some time after the ordeal.

Over and over, I kept meandering down the same path, dictating questions in my mind. How could this have happened? What kind of justice was this? We all knew the man was guilty. I had promised my daughter that if she told the truth in court, her daddy would be put behind bars. From what was told to me, she did this and she did a damned good job. How will she ever trust me again? I was so angry. My poor baby! She always had to struggle and fend herself against other people laughing and gawking at her because of her learning problems. Now this! How would she survive the trauma she had undergone and grow up realizing her daddy, the criminal, was set free.

My greatest wish was that he would get imprisoned with other perverts like himself. Then he should be tortured, threatened, and humiliated just like he had done to Katie and Mark. Little did I know it would never happen; it was over.

My father had been a warden of a maximum correctional facility for about twenty years. Thank God, he passed away before all of this happened. He loved his two grandchildren more than life itself. Daddy had played a tremendous role in my exhusband getting his fine, upstanding job with the Va. Dept. of Corrections. After finding out that D.L. betrayed me, Daddy hated him. He had brought embarrassment and humility to my family. God forbid, should he have lived to see what this scoundrel had done to his grandchildren and gotten away with.

What Follows?

Chapter Twelve

My school year as a continuing sixth grade history teacher got off to a fairly smooth start, considering all that had happened. I missed my first two work-days of school by being in court. However, I had already gone into my class-room several days before the trial to clean up and decorate the classroom walls in preparation for the new group of rising sixth graders. Most everything was set well into place. Once I returned to work, all I had to do was get with my team teachers and get the students grouped for classes.

Once the students arrived the day after Labor Day, I could tell that I had a "good crop" of students that year. Most of them were functioning average to above average in academics. Of course, this particular school year, our school was venturing out and taking a major schoolwide role of inclusion. Inclusion was a term given to the act of mainstreaming special education students or students with handicapping and/or behavioral problems into the regular classrooms. There would no longer be separate small-group classes for children who were classified as learning disabled or moderately emotionally disturbed. These children would have a special education teacher who traveled with them all day into regular classroom settings. The special education teacher and the regular education teacher were supposed to collaborate or co-teach these handicapped children. Of course, the special education teacher was actually in my classroom only one period a day when the handicapped students came to history. For the remainder of the day, she went with these children to their other classes. Inclusion was a concept very new to our school but actually a very old term for anyone such as myself, who had worked in special education for over twenty years. I served as a learning disabilities teacher in Southampton County Public Schools for approximately two years prior to moving to Greensville county schools.

Katie was going to be in the seventh grade at E.W. Wyatt Middle School and Mark was entering his junior year at Greensville County High School. I was headed into my twenty-fourth year of teaching and Mike in his thirteenth year of carpentry.

Mr. Edwards had made contact, and we met with him one last time. He told us that the Commonwealth's Attorney, Mr. Grizzard, had decided that it would not be to our best interest to pursue the new charges Mark had brought up against his father. Most of the reasoning behind not pursuing this was because Mark had gone for so long and denied anything had happened between he and his father.

The months following the trial seemed to flow smoothly in all aspects. Mike and I, my mother, and the children all worked together in attempting to put the past behind us and move forward day by day.

Mike was continuing his job with building houses for Mr. Proctor of A.G. Proctor Corporation. For the past couple of years, Mr. Proctor's health had been declining. However his wife, Wanda, worked closely with the business so she was able to handle the newly approved project of buying land to accommodate thirty houses, one house per lot. My husband was the supervisor in charge of building the thirty houses.

Mother and Charlie, my new stepfather, had their ups and downs even at their ripe old ages of seventy-one and seventy-five. Usually, Charlie would get fed up with my mother's constant ridicule about his behavior or appearance until he would finally return to his home Kentucky.

Mother would not go either because of her stubbornness, or total devotion and dedication to her bed-ridden sister, Virginia Bowen. Aunt Virginia had Parkinson's disease and resided in a neighboring nursing home in Franklin, Virginia. She and my mother were the two girls in the Fox family. The two sisters and two brothers were born to my grandmother, Kate Collins and grandfather, Jethro Ward Fox, Sr. My maternal grandparents bought an old school house in Adams Grove, Virginia and that is where the four children grew up. My grandfather was a farmer and my grandmother did sewing for the neighborhood community. My mother always said Mama Kate was the best seamstress around.

I never knew Daddy Jett, my maternal grandfather, because he died in his sleep when I was only two years old. Mama Kate, as I called her, lived until I was a junior in college and died on my twenty-third birthday, June 19, 1978.

My paternal grandmother, Patsy Kelly, died of cancer before I was born. She was only in her fifties. My paternal grandfather, Alonzo Kelly, died when I was very young somewhere between my sixth and tenth birthday. I remember 'Pop,' as they called him because of his total isolation from my father and my father's sister, Elizabeth. He lived in his own little world never speaking to anyone. He only sat in his rocking chair next to the wood heater and chewed tobacco. When the family gathered at my aunt's for Christmas, he still spoke rarely to anyone.

At any rate, the escapades with Mother and Charlie began occurring more frequently, usually, about once a month. Inevitably, however, they would reconcile by phone and usually Charlie would return to Adams Grove until the next spat. Sometimes Mother would travel to Kentucky with Charlie and stay for a couple of weeks, but nothing long term because she hated to leave her sister.

Whenever I questioned my mother about the continuous mishaps between she and Charlie, she would always be very protective of him and claim that he loved her and she loved him no matter how much their actions seemed to prove otherwise. I very quickly got the message that I needed to cease the interrogation and move on to other topics.

A New Terror

Chapter Thirteen

It was November 2003 and the holiday season was rapidly approaching. D.L. had luckily stayed his distance from the children with no attempts to make contact whatsoever.

One Saturday, November 19th, I decided to make a trip to Southpark Mall for Christmas shopping. The mall was a popular place for shopping at any time of year. It was about a forty-five minute drive and I had decided to make a day of it. My weekend plans also included a promise to the kids to begin decorating for Christmas on Sunday, the next day.

My stomach had not been feeling well for several weeks. I was having problems with bloatedness and constipation as well as taking laxatives every other day. On this particular Saturday, I did not take time to eat during the day because of my stomach problems and I was trying to diet at the same time.

After a day of shopping, I returned home near the dinner hour around 5:30 or 6:00pm. My husband had started supper. He fixed me a "Greensville County Martini," so he called it, with Sundrop and bourbon. We generally had one or two drinks in the evening before and after our meal. Because of my continued stomach discomfort, I took a couple of laxatives in one last attempt to relieve the bloated feeling. Approximately five to ten minutes later, while sitting down to relax, my stomach began to hurt. It lingered until it was no longer a discomfort, but full-fledge chronic pain. The pain was to my lower abdomen. At first, I thought perhaps I was just having severe gas pains, but my condition worsened. I mentioned the pain to my husband when it began. He had prepared one of his famous "super" tossed salads with tomato, cucumbers, ham, egg, and noodles among other things. He always made healthy salads. I thought I should eat a few mouthfuls, thinking maybe I needed some substance to counteract the laxatives.

Very quickly, I realized that I had made a mistake. Following the second or third bite of the salad, the pain became so excruciating that I stopped and told my husband that he needed to get me to the emergency room as quickly as possible.

We arrived at the emergency room of Greensville Memorial Hospital at approximately 8:00 P.M..As I sat in the waiting room doubled over with pain, I kept saying to my husband, "What is taking them so long? Why don't they call me back?" The thirty minutes, or longer, of waiting seemed like an eternity.

My concerned husband kept patting me on the back until finally he asked the receptionist, ""When will the nurse call her back? The pain is getting worse!"

The nurse responded, "There is a baby who is having trouble breathing, sir. Your wife will be next."

Quite naturally, this shut us both up for the moment. Then, almost as quickly as the nurse finished up her last words, another nurse came to the door and called us back.

After a very brief examination by the intern doctor on call for the weekend, I was diagnosed with having a urinary track infection. I had also been told before the final diagnosis that I would be getting an x-ray which I never received.

My husband and I left the hospital with two prescriptions that were filled at a local drugstore before our return trip home.

The next two days were long. My stomach pain was not as severe, but the discomfort was still prevalent. I did not go to work on Monday, and by that evening, as I lay flat on my back, I suggested to my husband that perhaps I better return to the emergency room.

Once again we arrived at the hospital ER around 6:30 P.M. This particular night, our family physician, Dr. Adolph Flowers, was on call. I was extremely glad to see him. After rehashing the events of the first ER visit on Saturday, Dr. Flowers ordered an x-ray of my stomach and urine analysis.

Following the tests he returned to the bedside where my husband and I were waiting, only to suggest that there appeared to be a blockage. It was not confirmed, but surgery would likely be needed. I was going to admitted that evening, as soon as they had a room available.

Dr. Flowers explained that Dr. Grillon, the newest of our two local surgeons, would be dropping in to see me the next day.

The Nightmare

Chapter Fourteen

It was late the next morning before Dr. Grillon, the surgeon, stopped by to talk. I confided in him that I was experiencing a great deal of discomfort. The night before was hell. They had given me an intima on an empty stomach. I nearly passed out after the nurse ordered the second dose. I told her I was feeling faint and weak. She quickly gave me a damp cloth. This seemed to revive me for the moment.

The next incident that had occurred that evening, was the torture tube. Two nurses entered my room and informed me that they were going to insert some sort of tube through my nose down to my stomach. The absurd part of the procedure was that I must swallow the tube to get it down to the pit of my stomach which meant I would not be sedated. I had previously, some twenty years ago, undergone this same procedure after complications when my son was born. The difference between the first experience and this one, was that the nurses in the prior episode were very patient and gentle. The nurses I was thrown with at the present time, were ugly, arrogant, aggressive wenches.

It was late at night and these two nurses had a major job to do. It was unpleasant, and I was the victim. They plunged the tube back and forth through my nostrils like a plumber gaveling a clogged pipe. The fact that I was gagging never slowed them down. Finally, in between their persistent pushing and probing, I told them to stop. I was not going to be able to complete the procedure. I had resigned to the fact that I could be endlessly tortured by these two half-wit nurses, or regain my composure and at least endure the stomach pain for the rest of the evening. The latter proved to be a much more inviting option for the time being.

The next morning, I did not discuss the intimate details of the previous evening with Dr. Grillon. Our conservation mostly centered around my condition. He explained that I may very well need surgery, but he would like to try some other procedures first, with my approval. I nodded my head, "Yes," in agreement with his offer. As the day wore on, I wished I had never obliged him in that decision. Food was brought to me and medication was given, but all the facts remain very vague except for the continued discomfort.

My stomach discomfort would not allow me to eat. I would take a few bites and have to stop. It was almost like there was no room for anything else to enter. I felt overwhelmingly bloated, and stopped up. As I think back, I have to wonder why a hospital would constantly shove food at a patient with a blockage in their stomach.

I contacted the nurse numerous times throughout the afternoon to inform them of my discomfort. They responded by asking questions and suggesting perhaps I was perhaps over-anxious or nervous. They began giving me medication for my nerves.

By three o'clock, I strongly urged the nurse to notify Dr. Grillon that something was terribly wrong; I wanted to see him as soon as possible.

A short time passed before Dr. Grillon arrived at my door. I told him I could not stand it anymore. Something had to be done. He offered that the only other option was surgery. I stated that I could not stand feeling the way I felt any longer. I wanted the surgery as a relief.

He responded that they would set it up for six o'clock.

The next few hours seemed rather long. However, close to the dinner hour, a nurse entered my room with a marker. She instructed me to take the marker and draw an "X" where I wanted to be cut. Dr. Grillon had ordered that I do this. I felt rather awkward being asked to do this because I thought it was the surgeon's job to do this — not mine.

I drew the "X" about midway my stomach because I was assuming an exploratory type surgery would be the answer to finding out the problem and hopefully, resolving it. This is pretty much all I remember from that evening, except for one more incident. I remember regaining conscience in the operating room tied to an upright board and throwing up. Then I was out again.

The next few days were not only a blur but a nightmare, especially for my family and friends. I came to, in and out of it. I remember flashes of friends and family entering my room, and I also remember not being able to talk to anyone because I could not get my breath.

The nurses and doctors continued treating my condition as they had been doing previously, as a nervous condition, or anxiety. Unfortunately, my nervous condition put me back in ICU about two days after the surgery.

Again, most of the events following surgery were very vague and not altogether memorable. Only when questions were directed to me, do I recall somewhat, but not necessarily on what day and time.

I remember being brought a portable machine. I was told to practice my breathing. I was never shown how to use it and never remember anything else about the breathing apparatus. All I recall was being so heavily sedated, I was unable to keep my eyes opened.

The Truth Untold

Chapter Fifteen

On Friday, November 25th, after arriving at Greensville Memorial on Monday of that same week, I was hardly alive. This is true to fact. I was back in ICU for a second time. Over the course of the past few days my mother, husband, and closest friends were hysterical, to say the least.

I had a very good friend who was a co-worker of mine at Belfield Elementary. She taught in the mobile unit right down from my classroom (which was also a mobile unit). We were probably the best of friends as far as our working relationship was concerned. Brenda had called, or dropped by almost every day I was hospitalized. On this particular Friday, she shared with my mother that perhaps she and my husband should think about moving me to another hospital. My mother and Mike had already been debating the issue.

Finally, when my mother approached Mike about the move again, he told her that it would depend on whatever I wanted to do. I remember my mother calling my name, "Sharon," she spoke softly. We are thinking about moving you another hospital. "'What do you think'? Is it okay with you, or not?"

I was extremely drowsy and totally out of it because of the sedation and my weak condition, but I answered, "Mother, it really doesn't matter. I am just so tired. It doesn't matter. These were the last words I spoke in over two weeks.

My mother requested that the 'Nightingale', an emergency aircraft, transport me to the renowned Medical College of Virginia located in Richmond, Virginia. However, they had no available beds. The doctor on call that evening, Dr. Bishai, suggested that he had a friend at Sentara Norfolk General in Norfolk, Virginia and he would like to send me there.

If I had been fully conscious, the helicopter ride would have been a memorable one because I had a fear of heights. I had never even ridden a roller coaster because of my enormous fear. It was my first ride ever in an aircraft and I don't even remember anything about it. It was not until several weeks later, when I regained consciousness, that a noise I heard in the hospital triggered a memory, a sound that for some reason, I associated with the helicopter.

The next few hours and days were very delicate and tedious, but I have only flashbacks of certain moments. I was unconscious for the next two weeks, so my husband had to relay all of the following events to me.

I was told that upon my arrival to Sentara, I had no vitals. My husband and my very best friend, whom I grew up with, drove to the hospital while I was being transported by helicopter. They arrived not long after I did.

My mother contacted my first cousin, Katherine McWaters, who lived in nearby Chesapeake, Va. and was a registered nurse at a local prison. Mother asked her to please be at the hospital when I arrived by helicopter.

Katherine ended up staying with me all night. She joined in and assisted the emergency team as they worked on me from approximately 6:30 PM. until 1:30 or 2:00 AM. the next morning.

My husband and Bootsie, my best friend, were able to get family rooms in the hospital only a few floors above ER. They spent the night. Mike said he could not sleep, so he waited outside the emergency room until the early morning hours when they finally came out and told him that I was stable. Katherine came out and kept Mike informed of the happenings inside the ER. She also advised him to get a pad and pencil and record all of the details as they occurred at the Greensville Memorial Hospital up until now.

The next day, Saturday, I was in a "dreamy" state of mind. I could hear people talking to, and about me, but could not verbally respond. Bootsie told me later that she felt total triumph as she and Mike prepared to depart for home. It seems she leaned over my bed and told me "Good-bye. I love you." To her surprise, I mouthed the words back, "I love you, too." She said she could not hold back the tears.

Mike did not return for another week. He had to keep working, and there was really nothing he could do. He said he called the ICU unit two to three times a day to check on me, but was always given the same answer: I was stable, but was still asleep.

Finally, one morning, Tuesday, December 4th, about one week and a half after being admitted to Sentara hospital, I woke up to a small, but firm voice speaking to me. The voice announced, "Good Morning, Mrs. Daniels."

At first, I was astonished because I saw no one in the room. Then the voice then spoke again, "There is a camera up in the ceiling near the doorway. We have a doctor observing our ICU patients twenty-four hours a day. When I leave, someone else will take over this position."

I responded, "I see."

He said, "Welcome back."

I answered, "Thank you. I'm glad to be back." He continued to explain that they could use the camera to monitor my readings on the machines, or just observe me. I felt good knowing someone had been watching over me while I was not unconscious.

It was just about six o'clock in the morning, but shortly after my conversation with the doctor on camera, nurses began popping in. Each one appeared extremely happy that I was awake and welcomed me back. Then the doctors, one by one, who were assigned to the team, came in throughout the day to perform their routine examinations.

During the course of the day, I found out from a male nurse who had been assigned to me, what my condition had been and what was actually wrong with me when I entered the hospital.

He gave me this information because I bluntly asked him, "Do you know what was wrong with me? Did I have pneumonia?"

This was the last thing I had remembered hearing at Greensville Memorial Hospital.

He was quick to answer, "No ma'am. That may be what they told you at Greensville, but that is not what was wrong with you. Our records show that you had an infection of the blood."

My husband called sometime that morning. He told them to tell me that he and the children would be coming, later that evening. I never got the message.

The day was full and exciting. I could tell I had lost a lot of weight. The first food item brought to me was a cup of chocolate pudding. I gobbled it down like it was a slab of meat. It was delicious.

Later in the afternoon, they began removing the tubes, one at a time. The oxygen was removed, but later returned because my nurse said my respiration lowered when they took it out.

I was also told they would be moving me out of ICU and into a room later that evening. My dinner was brought in around 6:00 P.M. As I began to chow down, I looked up and to my pleasant surprise saw my husband, Mike, and my two children, Mark and Katie all piling up into my room. J.L., my husband's nephew, had brought them. I was ecstatic. I grabbed my husband's hand, cried, "I'm so glad to see you, "Sir. I missed you so much. I'm so glad you came."

I called my husband, "Sir," as a nickname. When we first met, he responded to something I said, by calling me "Ma'am." From that time on, I just said" Sir" when I addressed him.

After hugging and greeting the kids, suddenly, a male nurse bounced into the room. He boldly stated, "Could you all please just step out a minute and let me get her covers fixed and help her calm down a bit before you visit?"

I really could not understand what had happened but apparently the monitors had shown that my respiration had increased rapidly due to the excitement of seeing my family.

When my family stepped out, the nurse quickly straightened out my covers and asked, "Are you alright now?"

I answered calmly," Yes, I'm fine."

My husband and the kids were allowed to return to the room. I kept holding on to my husband's hand as if I would never get the chance to do it again.

In what seemed like only a short period of time, my family had to leave. The children had to go to school the next day.

Not long after they left, my cousin, Katherine and her husband, Cliff arrived. She was extremely excited to see me awake. She proceeded to tell me that she and Cliff had been slipping in every night for the past two weeks to check on me. I was always asleep. The three of us had a nice visit. I truly appreciated all that she had done for me, though I had not been aware of any of it until the visit that evening.

When they left, the nurse came to tell me I was being moved out of ICU to a room. I was extremely happy, but rather tired by the time they came to make the move. It was a little after 9:00 P.M.

"A New Beginning"

Chapter Sixteen

My new room was nice and roomy. It was a corner room at the end of the hall on the sixth floor. There was a small inlet off the Chesapeake Bay that could be seen from my room. It had a ship dock with a couple of cranes on it. I spent most of my waking moments for the next few days, just staring out the window and watching T.V.

Mike did not return until later that week when he was to take me home. On Thursday, December 5, 2003 the doctor passed by my room between 9:00 and 9:30 P.M. and saw I was awake watching T.V. He entered and told me to get up early the next morning and prepare to go home. I would likely be discharged around mid-morning. He also said they would be removing the IVs later on that evening. After the doctor left, I immediately called Mike. He seemed questioningly surprised, but calm. He just told me to call him when I knew for sure what time I would be leaving the next morning. It took about an hour to get to the hospital from our home in Emporia. I told him good night and I loved him.

That night, I did not sleep. I watched movies and re-runs of the Andy Griffith show. The night nurse was very patient. She would drop in from time to time and chat. I suppose she sensed my anxiousness. Finally, she offered to give me two Tylenol tablets which I gratefully accepted. It made me a little drowsy, but I never really fell into a deep sleep for the rest of the night.

The next day was a long one. I was up and getting my shower by 6:00A.M. An occupational therapist assisted me with the shower and washing my hair. It was so refreshing to feel the vibrant water rushing over my body after such a long period of time. A portable hose was available in the shower so I could "wash my hair and hold on to the shower rail simultaneously. The therapist had a chair ready for me to sit in while I dried my hair.

Following the bath, breakfast was then brought to me. Most of the time, they served eggs, sausage, and biscuit. It was delicious, but I could only eat a few bites. I had lost about twenty pounds since I was first admitted to the hospital in Emporia.

The morning was very agonizing. I kept waiting for the doctor to enter and give me the discharge, but it never happened. I repeatedly asked the nurses when the doctor was coming. They just said he was tied up and would be in later.

Along with the endless wait, a student nurse practitioner was assigned to me. I was asked permission for this assignment very early that morning. Being a teacher, I never thought twice about giving the approval.

Throughout the morning the young practitioner was in and out, giving me shots, or taking blood. At one point, I nearly passed out while he was trying to flush out one of the tubes. He had to let me rest a few minutes before he was able to finish the procedure.

Soon it was time for lunch and still no doctor, I had called Mike around eleven o'clock to fill him in on what was happening—no doctor, no discharge. I laid down to rest after lunch because I was tired. Just as I had gotten settled down to rest, a nurse brought in another IV. She said I needed something to give me a little energy for the trip home. By this time, I wondered if home was ever going to be a reality.

Finally, around two o'clock, the nurse came in and told me the doctor had called and explained that he had been tied up in a meeting. He would arrive at the hospital in about an hour. Sure enough, he did arrive in about an hour and proceeded to tell me he wanted the physical therapist to examine me before I was discharged.

Shortly after he left, two ladies arrived. One was the therapist and the other was her assistant. They told me they were going to take me for a walk. They asked if I wanted to use a walker, or a cane. I requested a walker because at this point, I felt like I needed all the support I could get. They walked me around the floor, slowly, but surely. We walked through a door. There were two stairways. I had to practice walking up and down a few steps so I would know how to do this when I got home.

Every now and then, they would stop and check my respiration and pulse. By the time I got back to the room, they checked my oxygen and I was in need of some. The oxygen tubes were removed later that afternoon.

Finally came the moment I had been waiting for all day. The nurse came in and said, "Mrs. Daniels, the doctor signed your discharge sheet. We have a few forms for you to sign. Your blood count is not exactly where it should be and therefore, Dr. Pamos has requested you see your family physician, Dr. Flowers upon Monday, or Tuesday. We will call and schedule this appointment before you leave."

I called Mike and told him the good news. He sounded a little surprised because it was so late in the day, but he told me he and J.L. would be there in a couple of hours. Mike did not cater to driving in unfamiliar places and that was why he asked his nephew to drive him to Norfolk.

From then on, the nurses were busy. One assisted in getting out my attire for home and another brought in papers for me to sign. Then two nurses came in to remove the primary IV that connected to my main artery. This device had been attached to my left shoulder when I arrived at the hospital, so that multiple IVs could be hooked up to the main artery without my being stuck by so many needles. It actually saved a lot of time and pain for the nurses and patients.

It took the nurses about five minutes to remove the device because there were stitches that had to be snipped and carefully unlaced. Once they took it off of my shoulder, I felt better because I could rub my shoulder.

Around 7:00 P.M., I was lying in a half-seated position on the bed when my tall, lanky husband walked in. He was grinning from ear to ear, and I must say, the image was mirrored. I was so glad to see him and to sense that I was one step closer to getting home. He leaned over and kissed me. We had to wait a short time for the nurse to bring the wheel chair because they had quite a few discharges that evening.

I was wearing a long, soft, woolen pink bathrobe tied snuggly about my waist. My warm cozy pajamas were underneath. When the nurse returned, I was eagerly waiting to begin my trip. Mike had told me they had snow back at home, but I was not prepared for what I was to face as we entered the hospital lobby. The doors jolted opened and this icy cold, blustery wind swirled around my body as if capturing my very soul.

Sure enough, J. L. was parked just outside the front doors with the explorer warm and ready. I was placed in the back seat where I could lay down should I get tired on the way home. I really was very exhausted, but I did not lie down. I was so glad to be awake—to be going be going home, to my family, my children.

Home at Last

Chapter Seventeen

There was still some snow and ice on the ground when we got home. It was dark, but beautiful. I was supposed to order a walker within the next couple of days, but with it being the weekend, I would have to wait until Monday, or Tuesday. Mike had to help me get out of the explorer. His big strong arms lifted my small frail body with much ease as he carried me up the steps to our doorway. J.L. departed after he had safely gotten us home. The next few moments were some of the happiest, most memorable I had ever had in my life.

When we got into the house, I made a 'bee-line' for the guest bath. The fluids I was given at the hospital were paying a toll on me. As I made my entry into the living room everything was dark and then suddenly, a surprise! Lights appeared out of nowhere. All kinds of tiny beautiful lights! Mike and the children had decorated the house for Christmas. The Christmas tree was set perfectly on the center wall in front of our three windows. J.L. had assisted Mike all day with moving and re-wiring the television on the wall up above our fireplace. It was just as I had wanted. All of the decorating I had planned to do the weekend I was admitted to the emergency room had been done. I couldn't believe it! I was in total ecstasy. It was like a dreamland. The snow—the Christmas tree! All was perfect in every way.

The kids were staying at my mother's house because we were not sure what time we would be getting home. They would be returning the next day. The rest of the evening was lazy and lovely. I was not yet strong enough to be excitedly energetic in bed that night, but it had been three long weeks since I had been by my husband's side. I snuggled up closely, my eyes heavy, and sometime thereafter entered the land of sugar canes and snowbears where all was quiet, peaceful.

The Long Road to Recovery

Chapter Eighteen

The next day, Mother brought the children home. I was very happy to see them as they were me. Mark and Katie got a little emotional when they saw me and we hugged. I believe they thought I was never coming home and they might not ever see me again. Mother was equally happy to see me. She always got very upset and unsettled when anything happened to one of her own. She visited for about an hour and then decided to go home.

It took the children a few days to get back into the routine of having me back at home, but we enjoyed each other every minute we were together. Christmas break was just around the corner, so they were even more excited about the upcoming celebration and vacation from school.

Early Friday morning, I contacted Mrs. Lee, my school principal, at Belfield Elementary. I informed her that I was still very weak and I would likely not be returning to work until January 2nd after winter break. I also told her that my family thought it best that I work only half days for the first couple weeks upon my return to work. She said that would be fine and she agreed with the family's decision.

The following Monday, Mother purchased a walking cane for me due to my inability to walk comfortably and steadily on my own. Also that same week, Mike took me to my scheduled appointment with Dr. Flowers, our family physician. He had already been contacted by a doctor from Sentara Norfolk General Hospital and updated on my condition.

Dr. Flowers appeared very glad to see his patient up and walking around. We talked for a few minutes and he noticed I had a little stuffiness. He prescribed a medication to prevent the cold from getting worse and told me to return in about a week.

I was still taking quite a few medications provided by the doctors from Sentarra and apparently the new medication Dr. Flowers had given me caused an allergic reaction. After a couple of days, I began having shortness or breath and dizziness. I called the doctor's office and he prescribed a new medication to remedy the problem. I was told to discontinue the first medication.

Mike and I did find time to get the Christmas shopping done, even though it took several trips to Emporia, our hometown. There were not many places to shop in Emporia, but we got the job done as best we could.

Once again, I don't know what I would have done without my husband, Mike. His patience and loving companionship were overwhelming. He usually drove me wherever I had to go the first week I was at home.

Most of our time at home was spent with me asking him questions about what went on during my weeks in the hospital. I was unconscious and knew nothing until he recounted the events to me. I wanted to know what had happened from the time I was in and out of ICU in the Emporia hospital, until I regained consciousness two and a half weeks later in Sentara hospital.

We talked about it only a little each day, because it was difficult for Mike to talk about, and equally as difficult for me to absorb and believe.

The second week I was home, it was only a few days before Christmas and reality set in. The reality of how close I came to death was quite an adjustment for me and at time, overbearing.

About two days before Christmas, I asked Mike to take me to the doctor. I felt I was having trouble breathing and a great deal of pressure in my chest. I thought I was having a heart attack.

He took me to see Dr. Flowers. Before they could call me back to see him, I approached the front desk and told the receptionist that I was feeling faint and must see the doctor at once. They immediately took me to a patient room as Mike followed. Priscilla, the doctor's nurse, entered, to find out what was wrong. Dr. Flowers was tied up with another patient and so Priscilla began to ask questions. I began to feel worse and I told Priscilla I was about to pass out. She began checking my vitals and my blood pressure was dropping. She quickly sent for any available doctor. Dr. Bishai entered along with one or two other nurses. He began checking my heart. I thought to myself –this is it. I am really having a heart attack. I heard voices, only faintly, until all of the sudden, Dr. Flowers was by my side. The tears began rolling down my cheeks and he quickly instructed the nurses on what to do. As the nurses prepared to give me some kind of shot, Dr. Flowers leaned over and told me "You are not having a heart attack. You are going to be alright."

They watched the machines closely, and a rescue squad was called. I became more anxious and as the rescue workers entered to get me, I remember sobbing and crying out, "I can't die. I have two children at home who need me. I can't die."

Dr. Flowers was at my side again and told me "Don't worry. I will be riding with you over to the hospital."

I responded, "You mean you will be riding on the rescue squad with me?"

He softly answered, "Yes."

For the moment, I felt a certain calmness and assurance knowing Dr. Flowers was actually riding with me should anything else happen.

In the meantime, Mike, and my best friend, Bootsie, who was also an xray technician at the doctor's office, were waiting in the hall watching to see what was going to happen next.

I was admitted to the Greensville Memorial Hospital and placed in a progressive care unit. I had seen Mike and Dr. Flowers talking, as they rolled me back to the unit. When Mike came in later to see me, I questioned him very reluctantly, as I still thought I was in the process of having a heart attack.

"What did Dr. Flowers say was wrong with me?"

Mike answered, "He said you just had a panic attack. There is nothing wrong with your heart. You are going to be alright."

Well, I was very surprised by the news, yet relieved that I was going to be alright. Mike stayed a few minutes longer and then said he was leaving, but would return later that evening.

Shortly after, Bootsie dropped in to see me. She had just gotten off work and stated she wanted to check on me.

She asked, "Are you alright?"

I proceeded to tell her what Dr. Flowers had said.

Bootsie responded by saying, "Well honey you've been through a lot. I'm just glad you're okay." She was always like a big sister to me and knew just the right things to say.

We chatted for a few more minutes and then she stated that she had to go home but if there was anything I needed to let her know. I thanked her and we said our goodbyes.

My dinner was brought to me on a tray. I was very hungry for some reason and gobbled everything down, cleaning my tray. I suppose not only was I hungry, but happy that there was nothing seriously wrong with me.

Mike and the kids dropped in later that evening. Dr. Flowers also came in while they were there. He told me that he wanted to keep me overnight, but I would probably be able to go home the next day on Christmas Eve. He also said that I would be moved to another room later on that evening.

Sure enough, the events happened just as he had stated. Not long, after Mike and the kids left, I was moved to a room and visited by Dr. Flowers early the next morning. After he told me the good news, I called Mike and was soon on my way home to be with my family for Christmas!

The Graduation Days

Chapter Nineteen

In June 2004, my son, Mark graduated from Greensville County High School. His senior year was one of the most enjoyable years he ever had in school. Katie, on the other hand, was not as fortunate. All of her years in school were very trying, even up to her graduation night.

In the spring of 2004, Mark had asked to go on his senior trip to Florida. I was a little reluctant to approve because he had never really been away from home in his whole life. Mark and Katie were never really asked to stay overnight with anyone because their school years were spent in special classes. They only attended regular classes with the larger population in electives such as Art, P.E., etc.

My son seemed very eager to go, but I felt I needed to remind him of the new experience he was about to undergo.

I asked, "Mark, are you sure you want to go, son? You've never stayed away from home except to spend overnight trips with your grandparents."

He grinned and answered, "Yes, Mom! We're going to Florida! It will only be for a few days. Coach DeLoatch and Mrs. Deloatch will be going with us as well as Mrs. Allen." All were teachers at the high school except for Mrs. Deloatch, who was a guidance counselor at that time.

I finally resigned to the fact it was time for me to cut the apron strings and allow my son to go on the trip. When I gave him the good news, he was totally excited. From then on, Mark could not stop talking about the trip. He talked about the plans, every detail, where they would be touring, where they would be staying, dining, and what night they would be returning. He even brought home and agenda so I would know where he would be each day.

Finally the big day in April arrived. I had to take Mark to the high school to meet the others and prepare to leave on the trip. I was a little worried at first, but his joy reminded me that I was doing the right thing. They were only to be gone for four or five days and he would be able to call once or twice while away on his trip. Sure enough, when he called, I sensed the excitement in his voice and knew he was having a great time. The trip was a success! Mark still talks about his trip to Florida up until this very day.

The warm, summer June night of graduation was another big step in Mark's life. He was again very excited and I was excited for him. Mike, Katie, and I all three attended. He was so handsome as he walked down the isle in his graduation gown. I, like all other mothers, was very proud of her son. His school years were not always pleasant due to the label placed upon him at a very young age, but he endured those troublesome times and now was ready to graduate.

I was a little worried about how he would handle walking across the stage in front of hundreds of parents and visitors, but he did very well. My husband and I also received quite a surprise when his name was finally called to get his diploma. You could hear all of those loud screams coming from the girls in the audience. I did not really understand why, but this gentleman behind me leaned over and smiling said, "Yea, Mark knows something he hasn't told you!"

The man just laughed and clapped as did the rest of the audience, so I just smiled and clapped along with them. I must say, I was one beaming Mama that night!

Katie, on the other hand, had a more disappointing and unfortunate school career. In fifth grade, she was thrown with another young lady in her special class that gave Katie nothing but trouble.

Lati´a was a little taller than Katie and she constantly picked on my Katie. My daughter was easy prey for people to pick on because she could be so trusting and naïve.

One thing Katie learned quickly in her younger school years was to fight back. She never backed down. She often got in trouble for blurting out, shouting out to another student who was bothering her in class. There were times when she also got into trouble for talking back to the teachers' aides. Quite often the teachers' aides would get into altercations with Katie and to be very honest, at times, spoke very unprofessional to her.

Being the protective mother I was, there were many times when I had to call the school and very openly give the assistant principal, or teacher's aide a piece of my mind. I was very tired of kids picking on Katie on the school bus, in the halls, bathroom, classes, recess, P.E., or wherever the case may be. Many times, Katie was coerced into carrying out the deeds that would also get her into trouble. Someone would tell her that she could be their friend, and then she would only turn around to find out that they were setting her up for hurt, or humiliation. Each time Katie came home crying and hurt about something that happened at school, I would hurt right along with her. It was so disheartening to see these things she was going through almost on a day to day basis.

All through fifth and sixth grades, Katie continued to be harassed by Lati´a. I believe that Lati´a was the bully to everyone. Katie's middle school years were not as bad as the earlier grades and high school years because Katie and Lati´a were in different special classes to my relief. She had a very compassionate Special Ed teacher, Mrs. Simmons, whom Katie respected and loved tremendously, and so did I.

Katie also had a very good rapport with Mr. Bullock, the middle school principal of E.W. Wyatt Middle School. He seemed to take Katie under his wing and looked out for her. Whenever a problem did arise from time to time, I told her to go and tell Mr. Bullock. Somehow, he always managed to take care of the problem.

Katie maintained enough confidence while attending Wyatt Middle School, that she wanted to be a contestant in the middle school beauty pageant. She was a very attractive young lady and I thought this opportunity would certainly give her more confidence and training if she participated. A friend of mine, who was the guidance counselor at the school where I taught, assisted Katie with her talent entry. She learned the words to a favorite song of hers, by Shania Twain, and Katie was to move her lips as the song played and also do a dance. Mrs. Barnes did a fabulous job of coming up with the perfect dance routine to the rather "catchy", but fast song. Katie performed it well. I was very proud of her. When the contestants first had to come out on stage in their evening dresses and say their names as well as tell a little something about themselves, Katie began to speak and her voice began to quiver. Suddenly, she panicked and turned to leave the stage.

Mrs. Simmons, her Special Education teacher, was backstage and literally convinced Katie that she could do the job and must not give up. Sure enough, Katie returned to the stage and finished the evening without any problem. I was so very proud of her, not only for returning to the stage, but really doing a remarkable job in completing the other events in the pageant. Of course, she did not win, but I do believe the experience was good for her and one she will never forget.

When Katie reached high school, this was a whole different ball game. First of all, there were no special classes to successfully meet her needs. Her academic level was so very low, at only first grade, that no one really wanted her in their classes, special, or otherwise. Most of the special education classes contained students who could read on at least the third, or fourth grade level. When there was an attempt to work her into one of those classes, the teachers always had a complaint. She was acting out, or asking too many questions. It seemed as though she did not fit in, anywhere.

Finally, there was an IEP meeting to make a decision on what should be done for Katie. Those in attendance at this meeting were the Special Ed. Chairperson for the school, the special education teachers directly involved with her instruction, the principal, and the parent. At this particular meeting, it was decided that Katie be placed in the class for the trainable mentally retarded. The teacher was Mr. Karl Anderson. This idea was totally absurd because Katie was much more mature, mentally, than the other students in his class.

The only reason I agreed to the decision was one of persuasion. It was suggested that Katie had very low self esteem. She would serve as a helper to the other students in the class because several in the class were physically handicapped as well as severely mentally handicapped. In the end, I agreed.

Katie remained in this class for her last two years of high school. There was no other place for her in the school. Some of the time spent in this class was worthwhile. For example, she was given the task each morning of going to the other Special Ed. classes, collecting the attendance cards, and taking them down to the office. I believe this decision did at first, give Katie a feeling of importance as well as give her an opportunity to get away from that class. She really did not like being in the class and she told me so, on many occasions; however, she did like Mr. Anderson the teacher, and Mrs. Lewis his aide. Mr. Anderson told funny stories, or made funny faces while talking, that caused the students to laugh.

On the other hand, problems seemed to occur many times when Katie was in the hall, at lunch, or in the bathroom. I remember one time, in particular when Katie when into the girls' bathroom at the high school. She had worn black jeans and a white shirt to school that particular day. Apparently, the white shirt and black jeans was a gang code of dress. Katie told me she went into the bathroom, and when she tried to leave, this girl came over and pinched her very hard on the arm. She then made some threatening comment to Katie about being in some gang. Katie told her she didn't belong to any gang, and she somehow managed to get through the bathroom door without being further assaulted.

This was just one, of the many incidents of which Katie was victimized while attending high school. Of course, she was also thrown back with Lati´a from time to time in the hall, or elsewhere. The most devastating incident happened on the night of Katie's graduation.

She, like Mark, was very excited about graduation and looking forward to it. Unfortunately, Lati´a ruined one of the most important events in Katie's life. Katie was dressed in a white skirt and white top as was requested for all graduating senior girls. She looked very pretty and I believe she was more at ease, than I was, on that June night of 2008. The seniors were all supposed to meet in the cafeteria upon their arrival at high school to put their robes and prepare to line up.

I asked Katie several times, "Do you want me to go in the cafeteria with you, Katie?" She repeatedly told me, "No mama, I can do it by myself. I'll be alright. Don't worry." So many times, I have wished that I had at least gone in the cafeteria to check on her. Then I could have prevented the events that happened next.

Somehow Lati´a was standing in line not too far from Katie. According to Katie, Ms. Wright, the senior sponsor, had spoken to Lati´a several times for bothering Katie and not leaving her alone. Unfortunately, Lati´a did not stop.

As the music began to play, everyone stood as the seniors began to march into the gymnasium. I kept looking for Katie. It seemed like an eternity until she finally entered. When she did, I was horrified. Katie had to be escorted by two teachers, one on each side of her as she marched to her seat. I noticed she did not have on her cap as all of the other seniors when they entered the gym. Katie was also sobbing hysterically, while trying to smile at the same time. I watched for a minute to see what she was going to do. When everyone was seated, including Katie, I noticed that she had somehow regained her composure from the time she had marched down the isle until she was seated with the other students in her row. There were two or three rows of people in front of us, then another isle that separated our section from where the seniors were seated. She was not close enough for me to speak, but I came very close to just getting up out of my seat, walking down to her, and taking her out of the ceremony. Had she continued to cry, I was prepared to do this. From the time she was seated until she had to go up on stage she was fine. Her name was called, she crossed the stage, and put her cap back on as she was crossing the stage. I still sat in astonishment and wonder as to what happened prior to her entering the cafeteria. Was she nervous? Did she panic when she saw all of the people? My head was continuously whirling with questions.

I kept whispering to Mike every thought I was having during the entire graduation ceremony. Katie luckily, was smiling by the time she crossed the stage to get her diploma. The teachers were no longer needed once Katie was seated after the march. I was very proud she had been able to finish the graduation procedures but was extremely anxious to find out what on earth had happened to cause her to get so emotionally upset.

Once I found out, I was more angry at Lati´a as well as the supervising teachers who were in charge of the graduation. Supposedly, it was almost time for the march to begin, when Lati´a managed to once again make her way back to where Katie was standing in line. She literally grabbed Katie's cap and slung it on the cafeteria floor as well as yanking off the tassel before the march began. Katie never found her tassel. This is why she was crying. She knew she was supposed to change her tassel over to the other side once she received the diploma. Katie was upset because she had no tassel.

Since the graduation ceremony was over, I felt I could not complain to anyone. All seniors were out of school and on their way to making new lives for themselves. What would the school have done to Lati´a? Nothing. This incident would have been handled just like all other experiences with Katie in her high school years. Most of the time, the administration looked at Katie as being the one who caused the problem. This was a day we will never forget. Katie's graduation from high school was a disaster all because of one troublesome bully---Lati´a. I began to wonder if a day would come when Katie would ever get a break from all the turmoil in her life. It seemed as though she was doomed for one big traumatic experience after another.

The Years After

Chapter Twenty

In 2007, a year after Mark's graduation, he attended a special school in Fishersville, VA. This school taught students a trade to enable them to hopefully get a job upon their time of release. Mark attended the school for a year and learned how to become a dishwasher. The school was so far away from home that we only saw him on holidays throughout the year. It was difficult not seeing him and wondering if he was alright. Every student who stayed in the dorms had to share a room with another person. No one was allowed to have private rooms. I was equally as worried about how Mark would adjust to this because he had always had his own room at home. He had some ups and downs but he was able to survive. We talked to each other by phone at least once a week. Mark was usually working in the school cafeteria on weekends and attending classes during the week, so he stayed pretty busy.

On the weekends, they always had special events for the students. There was a student center, or building where students could hang out when there was nothing else for them to do. Mark said it was beautiful. It had a large stone fireplace, large T.V., and usually refreshments were always available. This is where he spent most of his time when he was not working, or not participating in other events. Sometimes, a group of faculty members took the students shopping on the weekends. Fishersville was only a couple of miles from Staunton, VA. which was a large city with many shopping malls. They also held large events like baseball games or other exciting happenings for the students to enjoy. One weekend, the faculty took the students to the Smithsonian Institute in Washington, DC. Mark really enjoyed this trip. He still talks about the things he saw in the museum. He will never forget this experience.

The last semester of school, Mark was able to receive OJT, on the job training. He was actually transported to a job site every morning, five days a week to work as a dishwasher. I believe he liked it, but with working all week and usually on weekends in the school cafeteria, he was worn out much of the time. There was some mornings he did not feel like going to work, or he went in, and had to return back to school for stomach problems and being sick. I do not know exactly how many of these mornings he did not work the full day, but it became a problem when it was time for him to graduate from the school. We had even gone to Fishersville one weekend to see Mark and make reservations at a nearby motel so we could attend his graduation and spend the night before coming home the next day. We were all very excited and looking forward to the event.

About one week before graduation, Mark called me at work very upset. He said his counselor from the school told him he could not attend graduation because he had missed quite a few days from his job training site. I was also very upset to say the least because I could not understand why I had just been made aware of this only a few days before graduation. I contacted the school and talked to his counselor. She proceeded to tell me the details as Mark had shared with me. I told her my concerns about all of us looking forward to his graduation and the short notice upon which we found out he would not be able to participate. She explained he would be able to participate in the fall graduation, but not the upcoming summer one. I immediately contacted Mark's job coach, Mr. Jim Rook. When Mark and Katie both neared high school graduation, they were assigned a job coach from the district who would assist them in making plans after leaving high school. Mr. Rook, assisted in getting Mark into the Fishersville school, and he kept in touch with Mark and myself during his year at the training school.

Mr. Rook came by school during my planning period the next day and we discussed what had happened with Mark. He had already talked with the school officials at Fishersville, but they would not back down in their decision. I had expressed my extended concerns about the fact that I thought Mark had just been overworked. After all, they expected him to work every weekend in the cafeteria, Saturdays and Sundays and then attend his job training site the entire week. He was working approximately six days a week, almost every week. Once in a while, the school cafeteria would allow him off for a half day on the weekend, but not often.

Mark would not be able to graduate until the following fall. He would already be out of school and at home all summer. I suggested to Mark that we find out if they could send his diploma through the mail. We were both so outdone that I, personally, did not look forward to taking him back just for the graduation exercise in the fall. He was not really interested in going back for the graduation either. It was like a slap in the face to the two of us. Fortunately, he did receive his diploma via the mail at the end of the fall session of 2008.

I was still very proud of my son. I was proud of the hard work he had put into his classes, the weekend school cafeteria job, and the work he had done at his job training site which was a dishwasher at a local restaurant. I felt he had done his best with what was thrown upon him.

Following Katie's graduation, she was not as mature as Mark in many ways, and I did not think it was best for her to go off to school. She could be easily influenced and this was a big concern when looking at the option of sending her away to school.

Therefore, she remained at home with us after high school graduation. At least I knew she would be safe, and both of us were so happy she would not have to deal with the daily problems and pressures of her high school days. She seemed very content to be at home with her family although it could, at times, get very boring for her.

Mark, on the other hand, was able to get a part-time job at a popular local restaurant in Emporia, VA. Mr. Rook also assisted in this new adventure for Mark. We were all very proud of him. He was assigned to being a dishwasher for which he had been trained. It worked out really well for Mark because first of all, he really liked having a job, and secondly, he loved seeing familiar faces come into the restaurant. He would often come home and tell me who he had seen in the restaurant during his work day. He always had a big grin on his face when he talked about his job. The only problem was he had no driver's license. Mike, or I had to transport him to work each morning and pick him up in the afternoon. This was really not a big problem because his working schedule was close to my school schedule, so it worked out very nicely during the school year. Mike and I always took turns on the weekends, so we could each get at least one morning to sleep late. During the summer months when I was off, Mike took him most of the mornings when he went to work, and I picked him up in the afternoons. Mike usually was about an hour later getting off work than Mark.

After several years of transporting Mark to and from work, I had a friend and a co-worker who agreed to tutor Mark from the DMV driver's manual to aid him in getting his driver's license. Sure enough, he eventually passed the written test after two attempts. I was very sure he would have no problem passing the driving test because Mark's uncle used to let him sit in his lap and drive on the secondary roads when he was very young. Also, his Mimie, my mother, worked with him and allowed him to drive with her when he was older. Upon receiving his learner's permit, Mother even taught him to drive on the highway.

I had one experience trying to teach Mark how to drive, and that was the first and last one. I vowed from then on, someone else could take the job. Mark was only about ten, or eleven years old at the time.

The kids and I had eaten lunch at Mother's one Sunday, after church. I can not remember where their father was on this particular day. We were getting ready to leave and I decided to allow Mark to drive us home. After all, we lived right down the road from Mother, only a few hundred yards away. What could it hurt?

I had a 1994 silver Lumina Chevrolet at the time. It was a used car, but a beautiful one. Katie was in the the back seat, Matthew in the driver's seat, and I was in the passenger's seat. Mother's house was on a small hill out in the country on Adams Grove Road. She had two driveways, one of which sloped down the hill. This is the one I always took to leave her house because it was closer to our home right down the road. As we neared the edge of the slope, I told Mark, "Start pushing on the brake, son, because we have to stop at the road."

The road was of course, at the bottom of the hill. Somehow, Mark did not understand the directions, or accidently pushed the wrong pedal, but he gased it. Boy, did we have one roller coaster of a ride! Luckily, we did not have any oncoming traffic because the next few minutes flew by like lightning, I mean literally flew by. If there had been onlookers, they would have cheered us on because we jumped the road and the ditches just like the General Lee on the Dukes of Hazard! It was amazing!

Finally, we came to a hault beneath an old hickory tree in a field across the road from Mother's house. Poor Daddy had been standing in the driveway watching the whole thing. He immediately came to our rescue.

Mark and I scrambled over each other to change seats so Daddy could direct me on how to back up and get out of the field. The front of the car was only inches from the tree, so we were very lucky that it was not disastrous. There was not enough room for any human being to walk between the tree and the Lumina. That is how close we were to what could have been a nightmare.

In the meantime, in between Daddy asking "Are yall alright, Sweetie? Are you sure yall are alright?", the shock of what had happened began wearing off, or just starting. Suddenly, Katie started screaming, Mark starting screaming, and I started yelling, "Shut Up! Shut Up! Yall are alright! So Shut Up!"

We did this all the way home. Everyone finally settled down, and their tears slowly stopped dripping as we pulled into the drieway. There were still a few sniffles as we walked into the house, but all was quiet for the rest of the day.

That was the reason why I left the driving instructions to someone else from then on.

In the spring of 2010, Mark was scheduled to take his driver's test. I was little worried, but was so hopeful he would pass it. Unfortunately, Mark had not received a great deal of practice, driving in town, and dealing with four lane traffic. He and the DMV driver stayed gone about twenty five minutes before they returned. She asked to speak to me outside the DMV office, so I knew it was not good news. Apparently, she and Mark had nearly gotten run over by an eighteen wheeler when Mark crossed to the other lane to make a left turn. She seemed a bit shaken at that moment, and Mark appeared somewhat nervous. He never got a chance to drive on the highway, or anywhere else because of his terrible driving in town. I was disappointed, but very happy they were not hurt, and relieved no accident truly occurred.

I asked around to see if there was a driver's education class offered for students who had special needs and had already graduated from high school. There was nothing available. We are still in hopes that something will come through to help him accomplish this goal. Once he is able to obtain his driver's license, I believe he will feel much less handicapped. He can the have the freedom to come and go as he pleases.

Mother's Return

Chapter Twenty One

In May of 1998, just a few months prior to Mike and I getting married, we were making plans to attend the Mayfest Day over at Adams Grove – Grizzard Ruritan Club. This was an annual community event filled with food, fun, games, and music. More music was needed this particular year and they were asking for more volunteers to perform for entertainment. I decided to ask another co-worker, who was a music teacher at Belfield Elementary, if she would agree to sing with me for the Mayfest. I had sung alto in the church choir since being a teenager, and was even asked to sing with another young lady for our G.A. (Girls in Action) program at church when we were around nine, or ten years old. I had been brought up in a family who enjoyed singing and music.

Rosemary agreed to sing with me. She was often asked to sing, or play piano for local town functions every year. We practiced at my house in Adams Grove several times before the upcoming event. She had planned a brief musical selection of summer songs from the sixties as well as closing with a spiritual, Amazing Grace. I thought we performed very well that particular day, and I was most appreciative to Rosemary for taking the time and energy in assisting me. It was an outdoor event, but a stage had been built just for the Mayfest entertainment. As we came down from the stage, following the performance, there was a very nice applause from the crowd. Some people were a little intoxicated and thereby clapped for anything and everything that was going on, but we all had fun.

My seventy-three year old mother and her boyfriend from Kentucky were seated near the stage with some of our friends from the community. Mother and Charlie had known each other since World War II. My mother was a waitress in a small restaurant in the local Emporia area and Charlie supposedly was some sort of mechanic who worked on airplanes in the war. He was in town for some reason and met my mother while she was working at the restaurant. Mother's heart was supposed to be promised to my daddy who was way across the seas in the navy. As it was told to me, Mother and Charlie went out quite a few times while he was in town. Mother even had a picture of Charlie in his uniform from WWII. She said he was a very handsome man and sort of swept her off her feet. In the meantime, my father was returning home on leave. So, mother had to make a decision – either Daddy, or Charlie. Daddy had heard of mother's escapades through the mail. A female who had a crush on Daddy had sent him word that Mother was seeing someone else. Once Daddy got home it came to a head. Mother ended up giving Charlie a "Dear John" letter, informing him that she must not let my father down. He had been in the service, waiting to come back home and see her, and they had been involved since their high school days. With that, it was all over between my mother and Charlie.

Surprisingly enough, Charlie just happened to find out about my father's death in 1996. I still do not know to this day how he found out, but I do know he called Mother after Daddy's passing, and gave her his condolences. It did not stop there. About eight months following my father's death, Mother called me at home one night. She told me she had been talking to Charlie for several months over the phone and wanted to know if I would be upset if he came for a visit. What could I say? I had been seeing Mike since October before Daddy's death and I knew how distraught and depressed Mother had been without Daddy. I was not going to be selfish. I knew no one could ever replace my father's shoes, but I also knew Mother had to go on with her life. Therefore, I told her it would be fine.

Charlie came in August of 1997. I was not at all impressed with him from the first time we met. He was very tall, and I suppose a fair looking sort of man to be in his late seventies, but there was something about him I did not like. Mother never really accepted my attraction to Mike either, when the two of us began dating. He liked his martinis, and Mother was very much against anyone who drank alcohol.

At any rate, Charlie seemed to find his way back into my Mother's heart. While Mother and Daddy were married, he sometimes dropped by the tourist center where Mother worked in her later years before she retired. It wasn't often, but consistent, usually once a year. Mother would say he just dropped in to say, "Hi", but he had lost two wives, and I assumed he was lonely and wanted to see my mother.

This never seemed to bother my father. Maybe it was because he knew how much in love and devoted he and my mother had become over their many years of being together. It also may have bothered my father, but he never let it show, to anyone, as far as I know.

I remember one time, the spring before my father was diagnosed with cancer, Charlie had again made contact with Mother at the tourist center. He was going to be in town for a day, or so, and she offered to show him one of the main tourist attractions in our state of Virginia, which is Williamsburg.

This is right next to Jamestown, where the first settlers came from England and made their home back in 1607. Jamestown was restored and appears today just like it did back in the early days. The people are dressed as they did back in that era, and they have shops and buildings to reflect the lifestyle of the people at that time.

Mother asked Daddy if he would like to take the day trip with she and Charlie. Of course, he had no desire to do so. Mother and Daddy had actually lived in Williamsburg right after they had gotten married. Daddy was attending the renowned William and Mary College. He was majoring in psychology and was only able to attend one year because my mother's father passed away. Mother felt obligated to return home and help take care of my grandmother. She was the only female child left to care for my grandmother because her sister, Virginia, lived all over the world. My Uncle Carl was in the airforce and they had to move wherever his job took him. This is probably why my father had no interest in going on the trip, or it could have been due to his lack of tolerance for Charlie. Following this trip, there was no more contact between my mother and Charlie until he conveniently called her when my father died.

So, after seeing each other off and on for about two years, here sat Mother and Charlie, together, at the Mayfest. Just as I was about to take that last step off the stage, the lady seated next to Mother shouted out, "Sharon, your Mother just told us the good news!"

I am quickly thinking to myself, now, what news are we talking about? Then the ball was dropped.

Mother spoke up, "Sharon, I hadn't gotten the chance to tell you, but Charlie and I are engaged!"

Well, it was a damned good thing my feet had already hit the ground because otherwise, I probably would have fallen off the steps. Trying to keep my composure, I tried to smile and responded, "Oh, I didn't know it. Well, congratulations, Mother!"

I never even went over to hug either one of them. I just kept walking until I found Mike. I was so shocked and astonished that all I could do was just relay to Mike what had just been told to me.

He resounded, "What? They're engaged!"

I answered as best I could, "Yes. Can you believe it?"

We continued to discuss it briefly, but did not want to make a scene at the Mayfest. When we got home we continued our conversation.

"Mike, I can not believe I had to find out about this in the middle of Mayfest. Mother could have at least taken the time to sit down with me and tell me in private. How could she do this?"

Mike continued to agree with me.

The following day I called my best friend, Bootsie. Her mother was a life-long friend of Mother's, and she had not even been given the news. It was truly a shock to Gladys, my mother's closest friend and her daughter, Bootsie. Our families had always been close since Bootsie, her sister, Linda, and I were all very young. Actually, Mother and Gladys had graduated from high school together and remained friends all these years. Bootsie and Linda were like older sisters to me when I was growing up. I had no siblings of my own, but they filled the order very close to perfect.

In the next day or so, I visited Mother and she showed me her extravagant engagement ring. She had even picked it out. It was quite a ring with a large blue sapphire in the midst of many small diamonds. It was a beautiful ring. There was no denying that fact.

The weekend before Memorial Day weekend, Mother and Charlie were married in our little home church, Adams Grove Baptist. Mike, Mark, Katie and I, along with a few family members as well as two or three church members were the only ones in attendance. Mother did not want a large wedding.

There was really no reception following the ceremony. The two of them just left and went home. A couple of days later, they returned to Charlie's home in Kentucky. Over the next few years, they made trips back and forth to Mother's home in Adams Grove and then back to Kentucky. Mother would try to return home every now and then to visit her sister, Virginia, who had been placed in a nursing home in Franklin, VA. Aunt Gin, as I called her, had Parkinson's disease. She had been diagnosed a few years prior to her hospitalization when she noticed that her hand would shake uncontrollably, even at night, when she went to bed.

I went with Mother several times to see her. It was very difficult to see her trapped in that bed. Aunt Gin had always been a very energetic person, hard at work, even when she was not at her job in Brady's Jewelry store, in Franklin. She and Uncle Carl had a garden every year that they both worked in faithfully everyday. She was also involved in several bridge clubs in the Franklin area. Her mind was still in tact the last time I saw her which was a few years before her death.

Approximately four to five years after Mother and Charlie were married, she just took off to Kentucky and did not return home until many years later. I remember she once told me that she was settling down in Kentucky with Charlie and would not be returning home except perhaps on holidays.

She said something about she had to do this. All of her life had been spent caring for someone in her family, first her mother, then her older brother, and now Aunt Gin. She told me she just could not do it anymore. She could not see Virginia in the condition she was in, any longer. So, she decided to move permanently to Kentucky.

Once again, this was quite a shock to everyone. Mother was not the type of person just to leave her family in this way. I remember having several conversations with Gladys, Mother's best friend. She would say, "Sharon, I just don't understand Cile". My mother's closest friends called her "Cile", short for Lucille.

She continued, "How could she leave her grandchildren and you? Even Virginia, how could she abandon Virginia this way?"

I just simply responded, "I don't know, Gladys. I just don't know."

Mother and Charlie did return home for Christmas a couple of years after her official leaving home, but then that stopped. I really had difficulty understanding why she could not at least come home for Christmas? We were always together at Christmas, ever since I was a little girl. How could she not want to see her only grandchildren Mark and Katie?

To make it even harder, she usually called ahead of time and got my hopes up. She would say, "Sharon, Charlie and I are planning to come home for Christmas this year."

I would respond, "I hope so, Mother, because we really miss you." Then inevitably, she would call about two days before Christmas and give me some excuse why she and Charlie could not come. Usually, it was she was sick, or not feeling well.

Mother and I usually kept in touch by phone at least once every two or three weeks even though she no longer came home. Each time we talked, I never knew what kind of mood she was going to be in. Sometimes when she called, she was in good spirits. Other times when she called, she seemed very down, almost talking irrational at times. Frequently, she would insist that Mike and I should move into her house into her house, at Adams Grove. When I would tell her we wanted to remain in Mike's house in Green Plains, she would get very angry.

Mike had two acres of land. On one acre, was our house, and on the back acre, he had built a very nice two-story shop to house all of his carpentry machines. Attached to the back of our house, he had built a deck. The deck was rather large. It surrounded an above ground swimming pool, of which the children and I always enjoyed many summers. On the other side of the swimming pool, he had built a trash room, small storage room for general supplies, and a sunroom. It was a beautiful layout for a home. We did not want to leave all of this.

Finally, Mother suggested one day that she would give her approval if I wanted to rent out her house. She said it would provide extra income for our family. I had already been renting out my house in Adams Grove for several years after I married Mike. The two of us made some mistakes after we were married with taking on a restaurant business. I had dreamed of having my own restaurant not too long after Mike and I were married. He was an excellent cook and seemed to enjoy cooking as much as I did. He had been in the construction business ever since he was very young and I had been teaching for many years, so I thought the change would be good for the two of us. The plan was that we would keep our full time jobs and Mike's nephew, JL, would manage the restaurant for us during the daytime. We would assist him as much as possible at night, or on the weekends.

The restaurant business failed for a number of reasons. We were inexperienced as entrepreneurs and made many mistakes because of this. Payback was even worse. We owed lots of bills as a result of going into the business. I suppose Mother was just trying to help us out because she knew the financial strain we were under. Therefore, we did rent out her house as well as my own.

The extra income helped for the time being, until it became more of a headache than a financial relief.

There were always repairs to be done to the houses and in the meantime, the tenants were not always as caring and concerned about keeping up the good condition of the houses. In some cases, they even caused damage to the rental houses. Finally, I just stopped renting out Mother's house because of the poor condition caused by tenants.

Mother and I continued to keep in contact over the phone over the next few years. We went out once to visit she and Charlie for a short vacation. It was very nice, but only for about three nights. I must say, I truly enjoyed the scenery from West Virginia on to Kentucky. The beautiful mountains and rolling hills of Kentucky were breathtaking. The horse farms were a popular site in Kentucky. Charlie was always talking about the Kentucky Derby. He and Mother attended a couple of times. If he was in Adams Grove during the derby, he was sure to watch it on television.

Finally, in late September of 2007, I received a call from Charlie. It was about 8:30, or 9:00pm. He told me he was in the process of signing papers for Mother to be admitted to some sort of psychiatric ward near Lexington, Kentucky, about 30 miles from where they lived in Lawrenceburg. He said he could not handle her anymore. It seems she had gotten up that morning and driven down to the neighborhood McDonalds, where he and his male friends always gathered for breakfast. Mother had entered the building shouting out and accusing Charlie of having some sort of affair with one of the waitresses in McDonalds. Not only did she curse him out, but also cursed out the waitress. Charlie said she really made a scene. Charlie said Mother had not been behaving rational for some time now, and this was the topping on the care. I asked Charlie where was Mother at that moment. He said she was being interviewed by a psychiatrist at the Lawrenceburg jail. The process had to take place at the jail because they had to question Charlie and have Mother tested before a final decision could be made. I told Charlie I really wanted to bring her home, but it would be a couple of days before we could get out there. I also told Charlie that I would like to speak to the psychiatrist once he completed the examination. Charlie spoke to someone while we were on the phone and he told me the psychiatrist would call me as soon as he finished with Mother. I expressed to Charlie that I was sorry about what happened with Mother and that I, to, had noticed some changes in her mood even through our telephone conversations.

It had gotten to the point that many times when Mother called she ended up hanging up on me. I always discussed this with Mike because I could not understand these changes in her behavior over the phone. I was quite concerned to the point that I even mentioned to Mike that I wondered if Mother was being mistreated by Charlie. Whenever, I began questioning Mother about how she and Charlie were doing she always said to me, "Sharon, Charlie is good to me and you must not ever think otherwise. He is a good man."

I would say, "Okay, Mother."

On this particular night, I had some feelings of sympathy for Charlie because he truly sounded like he was at the end of the rope. He did not know what else to do with Mother. I thanked him for calling and told him I would be in touch once we got to Kentucky.

About forty-five minutes later, the psychiatrist from the Lawrenceburg jail called. He was very nice and told me he would like to ask me a few questions regarding Mother's history and what was happening with her at the present. I explained to him that I had not seen Mother for a while, but we kept in touch by telephone about once every two weeks. I also told him that I had noticed some irrational behavior and mood swings each time we talked on phone.

I said it had become increasingly worse over about the past year and I could not understand the change that had come over her. I told him I was very concerned about this episode with Mother, but I wanted to come and get her and bring her home with me, to Virginia, just as soon as my husband and I could make the arrangements. We both had jobs and someone would have to take care of Mark and Katie. I continued to explain to the gentleman that Mother was a southern lady and I really did not want her placed in some mental hospital. She was very refined and I thought she would be most uncomfortable in one of those places.

He was very understanding of the circumstances. He said what he would like to do was place mother in some sort of a healing hands home in Harrisburg, Kentucky, just about a 15 mile drive from Lawrenceburg. He said it was like a hospital, because there was at least one or two doctors at the facility during the day and nurses were there day and night to care for the patients. It only housed a few patients at a time, who needed immediate care and a place to stay until a family member could come and get them. He also told me the doctor's name who would be caring for Mother while she was there. He would be observing her and conducting some tests on her for the next day, or so, until we arrived. Then he would go over the test results with me once we got there, so I would have some idea of what was going on before we left for the journey home. He suggested I call the facility the next day, or when I had a better idea of the exact day we would be arriving. I told him I would be glad to do so, and that I would probably want to call and check on Mother the next day, anyway.

Mike and I had a lot of plans and phone calls to make in a short amount of time, but we were able to leave two days after I had gotten the call from Charlie. Once again, I called my best friend, Bootsie. I relayed the details with her and told her I needed to ask her a big favor. I asked if she could take care of Mark and Katie while we went to Kentucky to pick up Mother. I knew it was an imposition on her at such a short notice, but I had no other choice. The kids were in school and it was enough that Mike and I had to miss work. I certainly did not think it would be in the best interest of the children to go with us, especially not knowing what condition Mother would be in. They really did not need their school routine interrupted either, because the new school year had just started. Bootsie, of course agreed with no complaints whatsoever. There was really no one else that I knew of, that would make the children feel comfortable, except Bootsie. They had grown to love her just as much as I had because they knew how close we were.

Mike and I only thought we would be gone for a few days, but in fact, it ended up being for the whole week. Once we picked up Mother we took her back to the motel with us. She had an adjoining room to ours so I could keep a watch on her and she would be close to me, should she need me. I had been very impressed with the home where mother was residing when we picked her up. The doctor met with me shortly after we arrived to discuss Mother's condition in private before I could see her. He told me he believed she was in the beginning stages of dementia, but he wanted me to set up a follow up visit with a physician from our hometown, once we got back to Virginia. He had called in several prescriptions to the Harrisburg pharmacy which was right on our way back to the motel in Lawrenceburg. He suggested we pick these up right after leaving the facility. I thanked him for his help and also thanked him for allowing Mother to stay there until we could arrive to take her back home. Then he said, "I'm going to take you to see your Mother now."

I had actually seen her walk down the hall through the glass windows from the doctor's office, but she had not seen me. I was anxious to see her for many reasons. I felt sorry for Mother because she was going through all of this. I knew she needed me and I needed to be near her as well.

When the doctor took me out of his office to see Mother, she was still waiting out in the hall as if she was expecting me. I softly spoke, "Hey, Mama."

She looked up and smiled, "Well Sharon, you are here," she spoke eagerly. "I'm so glad to see you!"

"I'm glad to see you too Mama. I'm ready to take you home now."

She questioned, "Well, where are you staying?"

I explained that Mike had come with me and we were staying in a motel in Lawrenceburg. She was also very cheerful when she saw Mike and greeted him with a smile as well. We gathered her few belongings which included her pocketbook and a few clothes that she had packed, or Charlie had packed for her to bring to the facility. The psychiatrist, or someone from the jail had actually brought her to the facility. Then we left to go pick up her medication and return to the motel for the night.

Mother was very talkative and quite happy to see us. She also seemed very happy to be going back home with us. We talked about a lot of things once we got back to the motel. She was still very upset with Charlie at this point, and truly believed he was having an affair with this younger woman. She told me she overheard him at night after she went to bed, talking with someone on the phone. She said he was giggling and carrying on just like a teenage boy.

Her conversation really made me begin to wonder if what she suspected about Charlie was true. I never found out because once we left Kentucky, Charlie was no longer a part of Mother's life. She did call him that night to speak to him and tell him she would be back the next day to pick up the rest of her things. Mother had already mentioned to me that she had to go back and get her things from the house and also get her car out of the garage. She wanted Mike to drive her car back to Virginia and wanted me to drive the explorer while she rode with me. I knew he would not agree to this because when we traveled a long distance from home he never wanted us to drive separately. On family vacations to the beach, I suggested to him several times that we had such limited space in the explorer with the children and our family cat, that perhaps he should drive his truck and carry half of the load while I drove the explorer and took the rest. He would always say, "No, we're all going together. We're not traveling separately." I usually agreed with his decision because I just assumed he had some special reason for wanting us all to be together in one vehicle. Therefore, Mike told me, in privacy, after Mother had made this suggestion, we were not going to travel that long distance home in separate vehicles. I sort of wanted us to be together also, because we were both traveling in new territory and I really did not want either of us to get lost.

The next day was a little unsettling for Mother and confusing for Mike and I. She was in a hurry to get her things out of the house, but she wanted to take everything she had bought for the house. I tried to tell Mother that we simply did not have room to take everything in the explorer that she wanted to take. We made room as best we could for all of her clothes. Other decorative items, coffee cups, dinnerware, Mother wanted to take it all. I told her we would make another trip out to Kentucky as soon as possible to finish getting all of her other items.

She finally resolved to what I was saying to her, but she still tried to pick up a few more items as we were attempting to leave. Once we left from there, we were all three rather tired. We decided to go on back to the motel and call it a day.

The next day, our plan was to leave Kentucky. First we went to the garage where Mother's car had been hauled from the police station the night she was committed. I did not get the full picture of what had happened, but apparently, Mother drove to the police station of her own will. Perhaps, she did not want to leave her car at Charlie's house and she, or a deputy drove it to the station.

The garage owner was very understanding of our situation. He offered to transport Mother's car on a trailer, to our home in Virginia, the following week. There was a fee of one thousand dollars for the entire trip. Mother agreed to do this and gave the man the check. She just wanted to get her car home as quickly as possible.

After we left the garage, Mother asked that we take her to the bank so she could take care of some business. I was asked to be present with Mother as she signed some papers to finalize all of her withdrawals from the bank. They had to call her local bank in Emporia to go through what seemed to be a lot of red tape just for all of her business transactions to be carried out. I am sure they were looking out for legalities, as well as follow proper procedure, since Mother was leaving Charlie and they were not legally divorced. Fortunately, Mother kept her financial affairs separate from Charlie's, or we might have had another very bad scene from Mother if her money had not been released. I suppose, being her daughter, this is why they wanted to confer with me and make sure everything was on the level.

Finally, we finished up at the bank and headed home. The trip from Kentucky to Virginia was about twelve hours. Mike and I had taken two days to get to Kentucky, and had planned to do the same up on our return trip home. Mother was very much in agreement in stopping overnight because she was extremely tired and needed the rest as much as we did. Our stopping point was about half way the trip home. Mother paid for our motel rooms coming home because we had made the long trip out to Kentucky to get her. I was glad because our money was a little low at the time until we got our next pay checks. Mike got paid every week, but I got paid only once a month. I had already used some of our extra money to buy new school clothes and supplies for the kids, as well as buy me a few things before starting the new school year. Also, this trip had been rather unexpected, one of which had not been planned, as a family usually plans a family vacation.

The next day, Mother decided she wanted to take us home through the mountains which was supposed to be a shorter distance than the interstates. Very reluctantly, we agreed to do so, but it was definitely a mistake. Mother ended up getting lost, thereby causing us to be misguided and oh boy, what a day! We traveled some of the most curvy mountain roads, up and down, up and down, for what seemed an eternity.

We finally had to stop a couple of times to get back to some of the main roads headed home. I had been calling Bootsie and keeping her abreast of what was going on each evening and chatting briefly with the kids each time I called. This time I had to call her and announce that we were going to be later getting home than we had anticipated. I explained about the shortcut Mother was taking us on and how we got a little off track. She told me not to worry, they would all be there whenever we got home.

It was the beginning of a weekend, Friday, so I was glad no one had to work or go to school the next day. First we went to the house and unloaded a few things to make room for Mark and Katie. Mother and I stayed at the house while Mike went and picked up the kids. Bootsie lived only about a mile or so, from our house and it wasn't long before the kids were entering the house and very glad to see all of us. They had not seen their Mimie in quite some time, so it was sort of a reunion for all of us.

In the weeks that followed, there were some happy times, but then some tense times. Mother had always been very controlling of me and our household when I was at home growing up, and now, she was trying to control OUR household. The difference was the house was not her house. It belonged to Mike and I. Mother started up her first few weeks going on this cleaning spree in our house, every day. While we were at work, she scrubbed the kitchen floor, more than once, washed baseboards, and just worked herself into a tizzy the first couple of weeks she was with us. I generally did the cleaning of my house on weekends, and I begged Mother more than once to please not do it.

I did not expect her to take on cleaning up our house while she was living with us. She finally stopped after the first couple of weeks because she was simply worn out. The woman was in her seventies. I had no problem with an elderly woman continuing to live and do chores as she had always done, but Mother had no business doing this. She had worked all of her life and usually had someone to do her cleaning and cooking for her for many years until she retired. Even then, she usually got someone to come and help her clean for special occasions, or holidays.

I guess I also felt a little inhibited because this was my house and I did not need Mother coming in and interfering with my cleaning. The problem was, I could not tell her this to her face. I was never really able to stand up to Mother. I always did as she wished until I grew up and got married. Even then, she had a certain amount of control over me. Also, I wanted her to enjoy her days living with us. She needed to relax and revamp.

The following Thanksgiving and Christmas was most memorable for me and our family. I invited Mama's nephews, Jett and Sam to come over for a holiday meal for both occasions. They each had a son, but neither of them had remarried. Jett had been married and divorced and Sam had been married and divorced. Sam had married his wife at a very young age and they had a son, Colt, shortly after getting married. Jett, on the other hand, did not find out he had a son until the child was eight years old. For some reason, the mother had kept it a secret until I guess she needed child support. Jett agreed to take the blood test to determine if in fact, he was Dillon's father and it was confirmed. From that moment on, he agreed to marry Cindy, Dillon's mother and be a good father to the boy, as well as try to be a good husband to Cindy. Unfortunately, their lifestyles were not the same and the marriage ended a few years after they became husband and wife. Jett still kept up his fatherly duties to his son as well as just try to remain close to him. At any rate, Dillon was usually able to attend the family meals, but Colt was not always able to come because he had to spend the holidays with his mother and her family in Raleigh, NC.

The boys were very glad to be able to reunite with Mother once again. We all had a very nice time together. My mother and our Aunt Gin took care of Jett and Sam when they were growing up. Their father, the brother to Mother and Aunt Gin, and his wife, my Aunt Bea were divorced when the boys were very young. The boys loved my mother and Aunt Gin almost as much as they loved their own mother.

The following days and months with Mother in our home was not so good. Mother was once again beginning to show some of her irrational behavior as she had done in Kentucky. I scheduled an appointment for Mother to see Dr. Anderson, a local doctor, the first week she had come to live with us. I was trying to follow through with the instructions passed on to me from the doctor in Harrisburg. I chose Dr. Anderson because many of her friends, including Gladys, her best friend, had chosen him to be their family physician. He did a few tests on Mother as well as requested her records from her family physician in Lawrenceburg. He called in a few days to confirm that Mother probably was in the beginning stages of dementia. He briefly explained that this was the reason for some of her seemingly irrational mood swings and changes in behavior. Her medication was updated by Dr. Anderson and she was to return in another month, or so, for a follow up visit.

Mother was beginning to make demands on me and Mike about small things at first, but then it grew into larger things. First of all, she really did not like the fact that Mike enjoyed his tardies in the evenings but she knew this would probably not change. Once again, it was our house and we were accustomed to our daily routines as I am sure she and Charlie were in their home.

Mother had mentioned to me several times when she first came to live with us that she wanted Mike to take down his deer head from the wall in our living room. We had no living room and den in our home, so we had to make one room our big living room, or den whichever you preferred to call it. I tried to explain to Mother that I was not going to ask Mike to take down the deer head because this was also his house as well as mine. He allowed me to arrange the furniture in the house anyway I desired and I thought he should be allowed the same courtesy. After all, the deer head had always been up on the wall ever since the first time I walked into his house. I really never even considered taking it down. If we had been fortunate to have a separate den, I am sure that I would have suggested to Mike that perhaps we move the deer head to the den.

Mother kept insisting that I mention it to Mike. I finally told him one day what Mother had wanted to ask of him. He very abruptly refused, "No! I am not taking that deer head down. It never seemed to bother you, and I am certainly not taking it down just to please your mother."

I tended to agree with Mike. I felt Mother was overstepping her boundaries just a little, but coming into our house and being so persistent in wanting to change something that was not hers.

About a week later, I got home from work and changed my clothes as usual before returning to our living room to sit down and rest. Mike had gotten home a little before I had, and he was also sitting down, resting, and sipping on his drink as he usually did when he got home from work. Mother and the kids were back in her room talking, or watching T.V. and so no one could hear our conversation.

He questioned, "Do you know what your mother did this afternoon?"

I answered reluctantly, "What?"

He said, "She came in here and tried for at least thirty or forty minutes to convince me to take down that deer head. She even offered me a thousand dollars if I would take it down."

Well, I whirled around with anger and surprise, "She offered you money to take down that deer head? One thousand dollars?!?"

He answered, "Yep."

I could not believe what I had just heard. It was so outrageous! Mother had definitely lost it. She was crazy! What was she thinking?

I saw the deer head still on the wall, so I asked Mike, "What did you tell her?"

He answered, "I told her I was not taking it down. It didn't matter how much money she offered me, I was not taking it down."

He continued "She didn't like what I was saying, but she knew I was not going to change my mind, so she got up and walked out."

I have to say I was proud of Mike for standing up to Mother. That was always something I had difficulty doing. Most of the time, I would just give in to what she wanted me to do because I was tired of hearing her carry on about it.

Another incident occurred not too long after this one, that also upset me very much. Once again, I came home from work one day, and Mother had taken it upon herself to remove all of my china out of my china cabinet and replace it with HER good china. When Mother left rather hurriedly to move to Kentucky, she left everything back in her house at Adams Grove. When she offered to allow Mike and I to rent out her house, we had to pack up everything in the house and transport it to our shop in Green Plains. I was so shocked to find out that Mother had taken absolutely nothing with her back to Kentucky. She had photos all over the house of me, her grandchildren, Jett and Sam, her sister and brother in law, and yet, had not taken any of them with her. I felt as though she just wanted to leave everything in Adams Grove, like no other memories, or people ever existed in her life. Now, she had gotten my son, Mark, to go with her down to the shop and find her good china. Mark and Katie's school schedule was about an hour earlier than the elementary schools, so they always got home much earlier than I did. She used Mark more than once to go down to the shop and haul things up to the house for her. She even had him moving some of her furniture up to the house for her to put in her room. This always really bothered me because once, she wanted him to move an old desk that used to be Daddy's when he was in school at William and Mary. It was quite heavy because it was old. She requested Mark go to the shop, up to the second story, and drag this heavy desk down the steps by himself all the way to our house which was quite a distance. The house was on the first acre and the shop was behind some trees at the back of the second acre. The shop was not close to our house. I remember questioning Mark about moving the desk. I asked if it really wasn't too difficult for him to haul down those steep steps at the shop and then drag it all the way to our house by himself. He told me it was not that hard. I don't know if Mother had coerced him into saying that, or not.

I began spilling off in private to Mike about what Mother had done with my china. It really angered me that she was once again trying to rule and run my house. I questioned her about the china. She told me that she thought her china looked better than my china and she thought it would be okay for her to do this. By this point and time, I was seeing a pattern with Mother. She definitely had a problem and did not see the problem. It was very frustrating for me because I was so in hopes that her living with us would bring us closer together, but instead it was pushing us further apart.

As the spring months rolled in, Mother was becoming more and more irrational. Her mood swings were much worse and the outbursts were more than we could handle. She also decided that now she wanted to spend most of her days in bed. There was no physical reason for her to remain in bed, other than she just wanted to do so. I kept trying to encourage her, "Mother, you must get up out of the bed, or you will eventually get so you will not be able to walk. You need the exercise."

She would smile and say, "Oh for goodness sake, Sharon. I am alright. I spent all of my life up on my feet working and now, I just choose to be lazy and relax. There is nothing wrong."

I knew there was something wrong, but the seriousness of the situation hit me when I went in her room one day to clean up. On occasion, she did get up, put some clothes on, and go into the living room while I cleaned her room. This particular day when I leaned over to pick up her trash can for emptying, I saw her morning medicine in the trash. I immediately went into the living room and spoke to Mother.

"Mother, you didn't take your morning medicine today. I found it in the trash can."

She responded, "Sharon, I'm not taking that medicine anymore. It makes me feel bad. I feel much better when I don't take it."

At that point, I should have made contact with Dr. Anderson and I did not. The dementia was a new experience for me and I really didn't know how much damage would be done if Mother stopped taking her medication; however, I would soon find out.

The days seemed to get longer with Mother's condition. I would come home after a long day's work and go into Mother's room to speak to her and bam! She would start going off about Mike being some sort of evil man and he was making me evil as well.

When I would question, "Mother, what on earth are you talking about? Mike is not an evil person. He is very good to me and the children. He has done nothing to you for you to say this about him."

"Don't tell me! I know you can't wait for me to die. You want my money! I know. I am not dumb."

I continued to try and talk to Mother even though I could not believe what was happening.

"Mother, what are you talking about? No one wants you to die, and we don't want your money. Please do not say that."

No matter how calm I tried to remain, with this abundance of hurt inside of me, Mother would not stop.

The more I tried to defend myself, the worse Mother got. She eventually began shouting loudly, more and more ugly things and cursing. Mark, my son, entered Mother's room, picked up a shoe, and threw it at Mother.

He was also shouting uncontrollably, "I hate you Mimie! You need to leave! I hate you!"

My attention was quickly drawn to Mark. He was having one of his anger tantrums. This was not the first time Mark had behaved this way.

There had been other times, since he had become older, he would get mad at Mike before Mother came to live with us. Mike and I would be arguing about something and Mark would enter the room, pick up a chair, or one of my flower pots and just began throwing things. If Mike went over and tried to stop him, he would just start hitting at Mike and one night, scratched him to no end. I would also began raising my voice at Mark, "Mark stop it! What do you think you are doing?!?"

After Mark suddenly came to his senses, he began crying because he would realize what he had done. I always made him clean up the mess when he had one of these outbursts. These did not happen but perhaps once, or twice a year. I just assumed it was because he had some sort of penned up anger about what his father had done to Katie, or how he treated them when they were smaller.

This particular night was no different except there was no one in the room except Mother, Mark, and myself. I again spoke loudly to my son, "Mark! What are you doing! You do not throw things at Mimie! What is wrong with you!?! Go somewhere! This conversation has nothing to do with you! Don't you ever do this again!"

Mother had the most shocking look on her face of anyone I had ever seen. She placed her hand on her forehead and said, "Oh, my God. What have I done? I am so sorry, Sharon. I had no idea I was upsetting Mark, like this."

I responded, "Whatever the case, Mother, he has no business acting like that."

I left the room to go into the living room to find Mark. He was still full of anger.

I began to speak to him again about his behavior. As I began to reprimand him, he walked towards me and literally grabbed me by the collar. I was not afraid of him. He kept raising his voice saying something about Mother and how she had to leave.

I quickly grabbed his hands and tried pulling them off of my shirt. I was also still raising my voice at him.

"What is wrong with you! Let me tell you one thing! Don't you ever put your hands on me again! If you do, it will be the last time! I will have the police here in a minute and you will never come back in this house again! Do you understand?!?"

By this time, he was starting to regain his senses. He had let go of my shirt and walked back down the hall to his room. He shut the door behind him.

I did not bother to enter his room and continue our discussion any further for now. I felt we all needed time to cool down.

I was very glad Mike was not in the house at the time. Many evenings when he got home, he went out to the garden while I cooked supper. He was not in the house while all of this was going on. I am not sure how he would have handled seeing Mark grab me by the collar. When Mike came in later from the garden, I told him everything that had happened. I told him what Mother had said about the two of us and what Mark had done.

He just shook his head from side to side. "I don't know what we're going to do, but something has got to be done. We can not continue to live like this. This is pulling our family down."

I agreed, but I didn't know what to do. I kept hoping things would get better. I really wanted Mother to live with me. I did not even want to think about putting her in a home, yet I realized that the stress and pressures falling upon me and my family were becoming unbearable. I mean it was one thing dealing with my son when he had those uncontrollable outbursts, but he was my son.

Mark had special needs and his outbursts were not often. It had become almost a daily occurrence for Mother to be upset with me about something totally off the wall every afternoon when I got home. Finally, I would just go in with a smile and speak to her when I got home. If she appeared to be in a fairly good mood, I stayed and chatted for a few minutes before beginning dinner. If I entered the room and she was not in a good mood and began going off about something, I would just get up and leave. I would tell her that I would be back when she was in a better mood. When I did this, she would get furious. She began yelling, "You come back in this room! Don't you walk out on me when I am talking to you! Come back here, dam it!"

Then she would began to cry, "Oh, I just wish I would die. Please Lord, take me away from here. I don't want to live!"

I would never re-enter the room when she began crying because I knew if I did, she would assume she was forgiven and just start up again. It was best I left her alone for a while. After all, I did not want to spark another incident again that would cause Mark to go off on one of his outbursts.

Mother rarely used fowl language in all of my life growing up. When I was younger, sometimes when she and Daddy got into a heated argument, she would curse at him, but I never, ever remember hearing Daddy curse in all of my life. This frequent cursing of Mother's was not like her at all. Of course, her whole manner was so unlike her.

I also found out that Mother was worrying Katie to death, as well. This was usually happening before I got home in the afternoons. She had begun to accuse Katie of taking drugs. She had it all figured out that Katie was getting drugs from someone at school. She even accused Katie of allowing some boy to climb into her window at night to come in and sleep with her. Then, supposedly, he would leave the next morning before everyone got up.

Mike and I could not believe it. Katie would become very upset when Mother would lecture to her about inappropriate behaviors and none of it was true. Katie would ask to speak to me, in her room, when I got home from work. When I went in to see what was wrong, she began to get teary-eyed, and proceed to tell me something Mimie had said to her, or accused her of, when she got home from school. Mother even mentioned to me some of her ridiculous beliefs about Katie, and how Katie was getting involved with some Mexican boy who was dealing with drugs.

I tried to explain to mother that Katie was not doing the things she was accusing her of, and she must stop with the accusations. She was making Katie terribly upset. We lived in a one story house that was not very large, even though we had enough bedrooms for each of the kids, and the two of us. An additional room was later built for Mother, and paid for by mother, because we believed Mother would be residing with us for the rest of her life. Mark's room was being used by Mother when she first moved in, and he had no space of his own for about five months. He had to sleep on an air mattress every night, in the living room, until the new room was completed. The rooms were not that far from each other and any sound made in the house during the night, would have easily been heard.

Mother would not believe anything I was saying, and her persistence would not stop. Katie had enough to deal with at school everyday without having to come home and put up with Mother's craziness, causing her to be in tears every time I turned around.

Finally, one afternoon, in June 2008, when I got home from school, I had just about had enough of this charade. It was destroying my family. It had to stop. Mother needed help, more help than I could give her.

Mother and the kids were in their rooms watching television, and so I felt the time to mention to Mike about making a change.

I spoke softly to him, "Mike, I can not go through this any longer. Something has got to be done with Mother. She is totally destroying our home. The kids are going crazy and we are going crazy. This has been going on for months. It is not getting any better, it is getting worse."

Tears began coming up in my eyes as I was talking, but I knew what I was saying was the truth.

Mike responded, "I know it. I have thought it for a long time, but I knew it was your decision to make. She is your Mother. I felt it wasn't in my place to say anything."

I told him I would try and call the Bloom Retirement Center the next day, and see if any arrangements could be made for Mother. There were two other facilities in Emporia, nursing homes, that housed elderly people for families such as ours, but I really thought Mother would like it better at the Bloom Retirement Center. It was more like a retirement center, instead of a nursing home. The décor made you feel like you were right at home even though they had registered nurses working around the clock. I would have to wait and call sometime during my work day because I could not take any chances on Mother overhearing my conversation.

Mark and Katie had walked by a couple of times to get them a drink, or snack, while Mike and I were talking. The living room, dining area, and kitchen were all adjoined as one large open space. There was a large archway separating the living room from the dining area. Mark, at one point actually stopped and whispered softly, "Are you going to put Mimie in a home, Mom?"

I answered quietly, "I'm not sure, son. We're just thinking about it, but don't say anything to Mimie. I'm not sure what we are going to do, yet."

He answered, "I'm not, Mom, but she really needs to go."

Then Katie saw Mark had stopped to say something to us, so she came in and asked, "What Mama? What did you say?"

I tried to keep my voice down, "Nothing, Katie. I will tell you later."

Nothing more was said that evening regarding Mother, or our discussion.

The following day, I was tied up all day, even during my planning period, and I did not have a chance to call the Bloom Center. Little did I know what I was in store for, when I got home. It was a nightmare.

When I got home, Mike was sitting in his chair, and I told him that I did not have a chance to call and check with the Bloom Center about Mother. Only a couple of minutes had passed before Mother entered the room in her pajamas and bathrobe. She had the keys to her car in her hand. She began fussing with Mike and I, with this hurt, but very angry look on her face.

"I know what you all are up to! You want to put me in some nursing home! Well, I'm not going! I don't know where I'm going, but I'm not going to any nursing home!"

She kept walking until she went out the door. I said, "Mike! Look out the door! See where she is going! She can't drive in the condition she is in!"

He looked out the door and said to me, "She is getting in her car. She is trying to start it, but she can't seem to get it started."

I shouted at him, "Well, go out and see if you can stop her. Do something!"

I quickly ran over to the telephone and dialed 911. The dispatcher answered and I told her we needed deputies at our house in Green Plains just as quickly as possible. I briefly explained the situation about my mother having dementia, and she was getting ready to get in her car and leave. I said, "She has no business driving. She will be a danger to herself as well as someone else if she gets on that road! Please hurry! We need someone down her quick!"

As I got off the phone, I looked out the window to see where Mike and Mother were. Mother had made her way around to the front yard, now, and she was walking down the driveway, still in her pajamas, housecoat, and slippers. Mike had started down the drive to talk her into coming back into the house. Mother was shouting and cursing at him. I then went out on the front porch. Mother was crossing over to the neighbor's yard. They had seen her. The man had come to the door and seen that Mother had perspiration running down her face. It was extremely hot this afternoon. He instructed his wife to go and get a chair and a glass of water for Mother. As I began walking across the yard to go and speak to her, she was seated and thanking the gentleman and his wife for their kindness.

I also thanked the man and woman for their help. Then I tried to talk to Mother.

"Mama, please come on back to the house. You need to get inside where it is cool."

"I'm not going with you anywhere! Both of you are stealing my money! I will never step foot in your house ever again! You are nothing but thieves!"

I felt like I was sitting on pins and needles waiting for the deputies. What was taking them so long? I kept glancing at the road, hoping to see some sign of a deputy's car.

Mother continued to sit. I continued to pace back and forth across the yard waiting for help.

Suddenly, I saw the deputy's car coming down the road. It pulled into our driveway and two deputies began making their way to where we were all gathered. Mother was still seated in the chair.

They asked for Sharon Daniels. I spoke up and said that I was the one who called. I introduced Mother and Mike.

Mother spoke up. "I sure am glad you all are here! My daughter and her husband are stealing from me! They are thieves!"

One of the deputies motioned for me to step over to the side where we could talk. The other deputy just stood near Mother and began chatting with her.

I briefly explained to the deputy some of the things that had been going on with Mother since she had been living with us, up until today. I told him we were trying to make plans to get mother into the Bloom Center, or some type of facility where she could receive the help she needed.

I continued, "I am not sure how Mother found out about our attempts to do something, but this is why she tried to leave today."

After a few more questions, the deputy told me he was going to speak to Mother a bit, and then they would probably take her on to the station to get a statement on what happened. He would need me to drive to the station as well, to confirm all that I told him.

I said, "Fine."

It just all seemed like a big nightmare to me. I was very upset and concerned about Mother. I wondered how she would react when the deputies told her that she needed to go with them.

The deputy told me that Mother might not want to go and to be prepared for what could happen because sometimes elderly people actually began fighting them when they tried to take them away.

I wanted all of this to go away. It was like a bad dream. I just wanted to wake up and it would all be gone. I did not want to see my mother taken away in a police car. I knew she might be afraid and feel alone. I was very distressed and had not wanted any of this to happen.

The deputy suggested I go on and get ready to drive down to the police station while they got Mother in the car.

I turned to walk away. Mike was still standing out there with them. As I neared the house, I glanced back to see what was going on. Mother was getting in the deputy's car without a fight. Thank God for her not putting up a fight. I am not sure how I would have been able to deal with that.

I quickly got dressed and told Mike what they had asked me to do. I told him I was not sure what time I would be back, but I would call from the police station.

It was a very long night. The deputies at the local police station in Emporia were very polite and understanding. Mother was in another room while I was being questioned about the events leading up to the incident. Every now and then, I overheard a deputy going to the waiting room and checking on Mother. He would ask if she would like something to drink. Poor Mama, still in her pajamas and bathrobe. I felt so helpless.

It took about two to three hours for them to continue the questioning and come to some sort of decision on what they were going to do with Mama. A psychiatrist, or counselor from the Crater Development Center in Petersburg was called in to finalize the official confirmation that there was a need for help in Mother's situation. He was delayed, or in the midst of some emergency when he was called, and then he had to travel all the way from Petersburg, VA, which was about a forty-five minute drive from Emporia. This was one reason why the entire night seemed so long.

During the waiting, I got ready to call Mike and happened to see a sign that read, NO CELL PHONES IN THE BUILDING. I knew then I would not be able to take out my phone and call him. I knew he was probably worried to death about what was going on, and taking so long.

After the counselor arrived and talked to me, he then had to go and interview Mother. He returned about fifteen, or twenty minutes later to my room and sat down to make calls. In between his phone calls, I asked, "What will be done with Mother tonight?"

He answered, "Well, what we are trying to do is get her into the hospital psychiatric ward tonight. They will probably take a few days to conduct some tests on her for placement in a home."

I told him I had wanted to place her in the Bloom Retirement Center. He said she may very well be able to go there, but in the meantime, further testing had to be done at the hospital.

I kept thinking about Mother in the other room. Her clothes were not very warm and it was quite chilly in the police station. I also knew that she must be warn out. It was going on 9:00 or 9:30pm and she was used to lying in her bed at home most of the time.

The time came when I had to sign some papers for all of the transitions to go into effect. The counselor told me not to worry, a deputy would get Mother to the hospital and make sure she got settled in, for the evening.

I was allowed to leave at that time. As I stepped out of the room, I peeped across the hall to see if I could see Mother. My heart broke. There was a waiting room for visitors, or family members, and it was filled with nothing but metal chairs for people to sit in. My eighty year old mother was alone in this big room, lying down across three metal chairs. It was a sight I will never forget. The tears began rolling down my cheeks as I saw her lying there, all by myself. I knew she was exhausted. She was mentally and physically exhausted. I did not go in and speak to Mother because I was afraid she would still be angry. I did not want to further upset her by my appearance, so I just turned and walked down the hall in silence. At this point, I believe Mother and I likely had similar inner feelings of loneliness, confusion, and abandonment.

I visited Mother every day while in the hospital to check on her progress. She was usually in good spirits. She also had a roommate, another woman, perhaps just a few years younger than Mother. They seemed to get along pretty well. I was so happy Mother was glad to see me whenever I dropped by. I made sure she got her clothes and whatever she needed during her stay at the hospital.

By the end of the week, mother was going to need to be moved to another place. I continued to express my wishes for her to be moved to the Bloom Center which was actually just behind the hospital. The question was whether or not they had an available room for her.

Sure enough, I received a call by the end of the week that the Bloom Center did have a vacancy for Mother. I talked to Mother and made her aware of the new place she would be staying. She did not at all seem upset about the suggested changes in her living arrangement, or the new environment she was about to encounter.

I took Mother over to the Bloom Center to sign papers and discuss the new living arrangements with the administrator, Anne Temple. Everyone was most kind to Mother and myself. There were several documents that we were to read over and the two of us sign. Mother asked me to just read through all of the papers for her. As I did so, I tried to take the time to briefly explain what each one was about. She still seemed to approve of all that was shared with her from either Anne, or myself. We had to write a check that day for everything to go into motion. Luckily, with Mother's retirement and social security as well as Daddy's retirement, the money was not a problem at that time.

Mother was going to be placed once again, in a semi-private room, with a roommate. The elderly woman was very nice and it appeared as though the two of them were really going to hit it off. I continued to drop by each day, checking on Mother and bringing her clothes, or whatever she needed.

About the third or fourth day at the Bloom Center I received a call at work. It was the administrator from the Bloom Center. Sure enough, Mother had begun to display some of the same explosive behaviors that she had shown at home. She had begun refusing to take her medicine and on one occasion, had even picked up her walking cane threatening the nurse as well as Anne, the administrator. They had taken her to the hospital for further treatment and proper medication

I thought, here we go again. Mother was in a patient room in the ER ward when I arrived at the hospital. She seemed calm when I entered to speak to her and was not sure what was going on. After further tests, the ER doctor asked to speak to me. He had spoken with Dr. Anderson, Mother's physician, and the two of them decided to transport her to a psychiatric ward in another hospital in Hopewell, VA. She would remain there until further testing was done. He gave me the name of her doctor at that hospital and the ER nurse told me how to get there. They were going to transport her that evening and I could visit her during visiting hours.

On the first visit with Mother, I did not like the hospital. It was too much like a psychiatric ward for the worse kinds of mental patients. I really did not believe this was the best place for Mother. She did not like it either.

The first turn-off for me was the oldness of the ward where Mother was staying. There were even bars over the squeaky doors to the elevator. I hated it and I hated that my mother was having to stay there.

Mother was in a dumpy room with a broken drawer on the sink. It was horrible. Mother had a young black female roommate that appeared to be on some sort of drug. She was always asleep when we went to visit Mother.

Mother was always in poor spirits when I went to visit her over the next couple of weeks. She seemed to be very uneasy about being in that horrid place as well as sort of afraid of the nurses. She would always say to me, "Sharon, you have got to get me out of here. I hate this place!"

I would respond, "I don't like it either, Mama, but they said you have to stay here about another week."

I could never really get a date from nurses, or anyone as to when Mother would be released. I had never even met her doctor. I was told he worked at one other hospital and this was why he was not always available when I went to see Mother. Finally, I got so fed up with not knowing anything, I demanded a number where I could reach her doctor. They reluctantly gave me the information where he could be reached, and I was able to call him on that same day while I was visiting Mother. She was extremely low in an angry and unsettling sort of way. I was very angry. I wanted her out of there as soon as possible.

After speaking with the doctor, he told me Mother should be able to go home by the end of the week, which was her second week of being in this god-forsaken place. He told me that they had kept her for a while, for observation, and to get her medication regulated before releasing her.

I felt a little better and even more relieved that she would soon be getting out of there and going, hopefully, back to the Bloom Center.

Mother was soon released as the doctor had stated, and we then began the trip home. Mother hardly said two words all the way back to Emporia. She asked if she was going back home. I told her no, she would be going back to the Bloom Center. She was not very happy. There were no loud outbursts, but very few words exchanged, mostly with me trying to explain to her that she had to go back to the Bloom Center because they were better able to take care of her than I was. This still did not satisfy her for the moment.

Once we got to the Bloom Center, Mother acted as cordial as possible. I went inside with her, spoke to the nurses, and then told her I would be back the next day to see her. I did not wish to prolong the goodbye because I did not feel it would be good for Mother, nor myself, with her not being in the best spirits.

Surprisingly enough, the next few weeks were more positive for Mother. This time she seemed to be adjusting to her stay at the Bloom Center much better. We had a few more obstacles to overcome, but nothing like the first time she was there. She ended up getting a private room because I felt this was best. She and the first roommate were not getting along to well. The change seemed to work well for the two of them. Mother went through a period of where she did not want to participate in the activities offered at the Bloom Center and often talked about how tired she was, of just looking at four walls all of the time.

I explained to Mother that she needed to get out of the room and go and mingle with the other residents. It took her a while, but eventually she began feeling more at home. Sometimes she would even look out of the window and say, "It is so beautiful here."

Mother has been at the Bloom Center from the summer of 2008 until the present, 2012. The dementia has gotten worse over the past couple of years. Mother lives in the past. She recognizes Mark, Katie, and I, but she only talks of people and events of the past, as if she were reliving the past. She does not always recognize Mike because he does not go to see Mother often. The kids and I go every week to get her dirty clothes. I wash them and take them to the cleaners for pressing because Mother has always been very particular about her clothes and how they look. It has been increasingly more difficult for me to drop in and visit Mother because she has begun to show those hostile signs of dementia. She sometimes curses or talks very ugly to the other residents, and when I see the hurt on their faces, this is very hard to chew. If I tell her to please stop speaking ugly to them, she usually whirls around and begins cursing at me. She is hard of hearing and is usually very loud when she makes a scene. It is not pleasant.

I try to focus on the happy times that Mother and I have together, even now. When she is in a good mood, I thrive on it as if I never want it to end. She will often begin to say something and forget what she is saying, or mispronounce the word and suddenly realize how the word has come out. Then she beings to chuckle and say, "Well, you know what I mean" or "Whoops, that didn't come out right."

Then she really beings to laugh and so do I. These are the times I enjoy the most with her. Being close, patting her hand. She looks at me, smiles, and pats my hand back. I will always treasure these moments because this is how I want to remember my mother. Being happy, smiling back at me as she pats my hand.

The End

Epilogue

As of August 2011, I became a retired teacher. It is an adjustment not having a set routine of getting up and going to school each morning; however I am still doing some substitute teaching. My joy is being at home with my family and spending time outdoors whenever I can. My goal is to pursue my writing career, perhaps even in children's books. I relax by gardening, playing with our dogs, Pepper and Belle, or going to the beach.

As for the near death experience back in 2003, I truly believe God was with me during my ordeal. I will always be thankful to those who prayed for me and my family during this disabling and traumatic event. I am also thankful to God for guiding the hands of the doctors and nurses who assisted in bringing life back into my limp body. As the old saying goes, prayer works miracles. I know from first hand experience.

My son and daughter are doing fine. Mark is now twenty-six and Katie is twenty-three. They both continue to reside at home with my husband and I.